Standard Grade | Credit

Physics

Credit Level 2000

Credit Level 2001

Credit Level 2002

Credit Level 2003

Credit Level 2004

Leckie×Leckie

First exam published in 2000.

Published by Leckie & Leckie, 8 Whitehill Terrace, St. Andrews, Scotland KY16 8RN tel: 01334 475656 fax: 01334 477392 enquiries@leckieandleckie.co.uk www.leckieandleckie.co.uk

Leckie & Leckie Project Team: Andrea Collington; Peter Dennis; Bruce Ryan

ISBN 1-84372-210-0

A CIP Catalogue record for this book is available from the British Library.

Printed in Scotland by Scotprint.

Leckie & Leckie is a division of Granada Learning Limited, part of ITV plc.

Acknowledgements

Every effort has been made to trace the copyright holders and to obtain their permission for the use of copyright material. Leckie & Leckie will gladly receive information enabling them to rectify any error or omission in subsequent editions.

2000 CREDIT

C

FOR OFFICIAL USE

K & U	PS

Total Marks

3220/402

NATIONAL
QUALIFICATIONS
2000

WEDNESDAY, 31 MAY
10.50 AM – 12.35 PM

PHYSICS
STANDARD GRADE
Credit Level

Fill in these boxes and read what Is printed below.

Full name of centre

Town

Forename(s)

Surname

Date of birth
Day Month Year   Scottish candidate number   Number of seat

1 All questions should be answered.

2 The questions may be answered in any order but all answers must be written clearly and legibly in this book.

3 Write your answer where indicated by the question or in the space provided after the question.

4 If you change your mind about your answer you may score it out and rewrite it in the space provided at the end of the answer book.

5 Before leaving the examination room you must give this book to the invigilator. If you do not, you may lose all the marks for this paper.

6 Any necessary data will be found in the **data sheet** on page two.

SCOTTISH
QUALIFICATIONS
AUTHORITY

LIB 3220/402 6/3/23120

DATA SHEET

Speed of light in materials

Material	Speed in m/s
Air	$3 \cdot 0 \times 10^8$
Carbon dioxide	$3 \cdot 0 \times 10^8$
Diamond	$1 \cdot 2 \times 10^8$
Glass	$2 \cdot 0 \times 10^8$
Glycerol	$2 \cdot 1 \times 10^8$
Water	$2 \cdot 3 \times 10^8$

Speed of sound in materials

Material	Speed in m/s
Aluminium	5200
Air	340
Bone	4100
Carbon dioxide	270
Glycerol	1900
Muscle	1600
Steel	5200
Tissue	1500
Water	1500

Gravitational field strengths

	Gravitational field strength on the surface in N/kg
Earth	10
Jupiter	26
Mars	4
Mercury	4
Moon	$1 \cdot 6$
Neptune	12
Saturn	11
Sun	270
Venus	9

Specific heat capacity of materials

Material	Specific heat capacity in J/kg °C
Alcohol	2350
Aluminium	902
Copper	386
Diamond	530
Glass	500
Glycerol	2400
Ice	2100
Lead	128
Water	4180

Specific latent heat of fusion of materials

Material	Specific latent heat of fusion in J/kg
Alcohol	$0 \cdot 99 \times 10^5$
Aluminium	$3 \cdot 95 \times 10^5$
Carbon dioxide	$1 \cdot 80 \times 10^5$
Copper	$2 \cdot 05 \times 10^5$
Glycerol	$1 \cdot 81 \times 10^5$
Lead	$0 \cdot 25 \times 10^5$
Water	$3 \cdot 34 \times 10^5$

Melting and boiling points of materials

Material	Melting point in °C	Boiling point in °C
Alcohol	−98	65
Aluminium	660	2470
Copper	1077	2567
Glycerol	18	290
Lead	328	1737
Turpentine	−10	156

Specific latent heat of vaporisation of materials

Material	Specific latent heat of vaporisation in J/kg
Alcohol	$11 \cdot 2 \times 10^5$
Carbon dioxide	$3 \cdot 77 \times 10^5$
Glycerol	$8 \cdot 30 \times 10^5$
Turpentine	$2 \cdot 90 \times 10^5$
Water	$22 \cdot 6 \times 10^5$

SI Prefixes and Multiplication Factors

Prefix	Symbol	Factor	
giga	G	1 000 000 000	$= 10^9$
mega	M	1 000 000	$= 10^6$
kilo	k	1000	$= 10^3$
milli	m	0·001	$= 10^{-3}$
micro	μ	0·000 001	$= 10^{-6}$
nano	n	0·000 000 001	$= 10^{-9}$

DO NOT WRITE IN THIS MARGIN

Marks | K&U | PS

1. Radio signals from the Olympic Games in Australia are transmitted to Britain. The signals are sent at a frequency of 6 GHz (6×10^9 Hz) to a satellite which is in a geostationary orbit. Using a different frequency, the satellite then retransmits the signals to a ground station in Britain.

Britain

Australia

(a) State what is meant by a geostationary orbit.

....

....

2

(b) Calculate the wavelength of the signals which are sent to the satellite.

Space for working and answer

3

(c) One of the layers in the atmosphere is the ionosphere. The radio signals pass through the ionosphere as they travel between Earth and the satellite. Radio waves of frequencies below 30 MHz are reflected by the ionosphere.

Circle the frequency that is suitable for **retransmitting** the signals from the satellite to the Earth.

20 MHz   4 GHz   6 GHz

1

[Turn over

Marks | K&U | PS

1. **(continued)**

(d) At the ground station in Britain, the signals are transmitted as a parallel beam of microwaves to a relay station, using curved reflectors.

Complete the diagram below to show the effect of the curved reflector at the relay station.

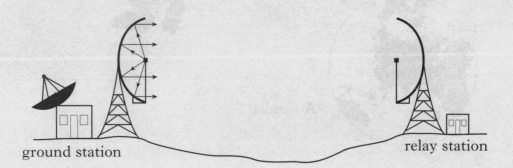

ground station   relay station

2

2. At a local swimming gala, the swimmers start when they hear the sound of the starting horn. This horn also sends an electronic signal to start timing the race.

At the start of the race, the swimmer in lane 1 is a distance of 2 m from the horn and the swimmer in lane 8 is a distance of 19 m from the horn.

(a) The swimmer in lane 1 hears the sound of the horn first. Calculate how much later the swimmer in lane 8 hears this sound.

Space for working and answer

3

2. (continued)

(b) As each swimmer finishes the race, an electronic touch sensor detects the swimmer's arrival at the finishing point. After the race, the scoreboard gives the following information.

Place	Lane	Time (s)
1st	1	20·52
2nd	8	20·55
3rd	5	21·91

(i) Using your answer to part (a), or otherwise, explain why the swimmer in lane 8 should have been awarded first place.

....

....

....

2

(ii) Suggest an improvement to the starting, or timing, system that would reduce the unfairness of the timing.

....

1

[Turn over

3. A floodlight is fitted with a 230 V mains filament lamp. The filament takes 0·5 s to reach its operating temperature.

The graph shows how the resistance of the filament varies after being switched on.

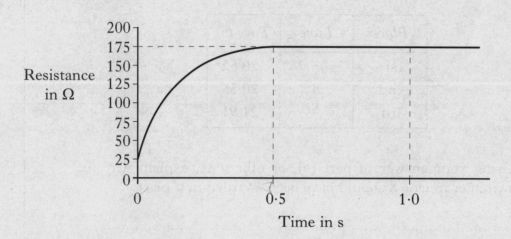

(a) (i) What is the value of the resistance of the lamp when it is operating normally?

....

(ii) Calculate the current in the lamp when it is operating normally.

Space for working and answer

(iii) The floodlight could have been fitted with a lamp with a power rating of 150 W or 300 W or 500 W.

Show by calculation which lamp **is** fitted in the floodlight.

Space for working and answer

DO NOT
WRITE IN
THIS
MARGIN

Marks | K&U | PS

3. **(continued)**

(b) The lamp filament is most likely to "blow" or fail during the first 0·5 s after switch-on.

Using information from the graph, explain why this happens.

....

....

....

.... **2**

[Turn over

Marks | K&U | PS

4. A lawnmower has a label which gives the following information.

> Happycutter Manufacturing Co
>
> Model HM96–150 ▣
>
> 230 V a.c. 50 Hz 1500 W
>
> Class II   BEAB approved

(a) (i) State why this lawnmower has only two wires in the flex.

....

....

1

(ii) State the colours of the insulation on the two wires in the flex.

....

....

2

(iii) State the value of the fuse that should be fitted in the plug of this lawnmower.

....

1

(b) Care must be taken to make sure that the lawnmower does not cut its own flex. When this happens, there is a current path from the damaged flex, through the metal handle and the person using the lawnmower, to earth.

A dummy is used to investigate the safety of this lawnmower. In one test, the resistance of the current path through the dummy is $5000\,\Omega$. This is approximately the same resistance as the current path when the lawnmower is used by a person.

4. **(b)** **(continued)**

(i) Show by calculation that the current which passes through the dummy is 46 mA.

> *Space for working and answer*

2

(ii) Explain why, in a situation like this, the fuse in the plug **would not** protect a person using the lawnmower.

....

....

....

2

(iii) What is the purpose of the fuse in the plug?

....

....

1

(iv) Water is now sprayed on the dummy and the investigation repeated. State and explain the effect that this has on the current through the dummy.

....

....

....

2

[Turn over

Marks | K&U | PS

5. Iodine-131 is a radioactive substance which emits beta particles and gamma radiation. A small quantity of iodine-131 is injected into a patient to investigate the thyroid gland. The radiation emitted is detected using a gamma camera.

gamma camera

thyroid

(a) (i) Why are the beta particles less likely to reach the camera than the gamma radiation?

....

....

1

(ii) What effect does radiation have on living cells?

....

....

1

(b) Two safety precautions necessary when using radioactive sources are:

- wear a film badge attached to clothing
- keep as large a distance as possible away from the source.

(i) (A) What happens to photographic film when it is exposed to a radioactive source?

....

....

1

(B) Describe how information obtained from a film badge is used to indicate the dose of radiation that has been received.

....

....

....

1

5. (b) (continued)

(ii) As well as these precautions, a technician wears an additional film badge on a finger when handling a bottle of iodine-131 solution.

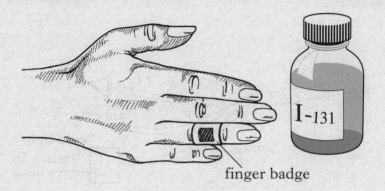

finger badge

What is the reason for this **additional** film badge?

....

.... 2

(iii) State one **other** safety precaution necessary when dealing with radioactive substances.

.... 1

[Turn over

Marks | K&U | PS

6. A health physicist is developing a system for measuring temperatures inside the body. A thermocouple is inserted through a tube beside the optical fibres of an endoscope. The endoscope allows the doctor to see where the thermocouple is being positioned. The endoscope consists of two fibre bundles and a "cold light" source.

(*a*)   (i)   Explain the purpose of each of the two bundles of fibres in the endoscope.

Fibre bundle P

....

....

Fibre bundle Q

....

....   **2**

(ii)   What is meant by a "cold light" source?

....

....   **1**

(iii)   Explain whether a filament lamp or a discharge lamp would be more suitable for the light source of the endoscope.

....

....

....   **2**

Marks | K&U | PS

6. (continued)

(b) State the energy transformation that takes place in a thermocouple.

.... 1

(c) The following graph shows how the output voltage from the thermocouple varies over a certain temperature range.

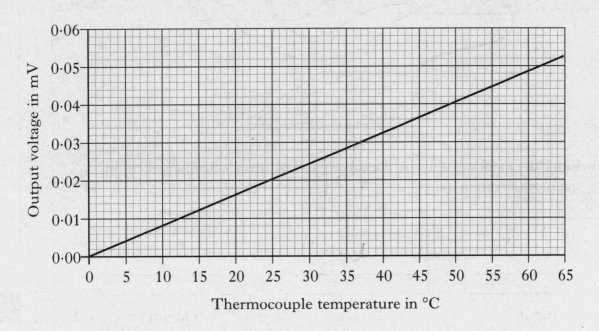

(i) What is the voltage produced by the thermocouple at 37 °C?

.... 1

(ii) The thermocouple is inserted inside the body of a patient who has a fever.

Suggest a value for the voltage produced by the thermocouple.

.... 1

[Turn over

Marks | K&U | PS

7. The electronic system shown is used as a light meter. A voltage is generated when light falls on the solar cell. This voltage is amplified and the output voltage is displayed on the voltmeter.

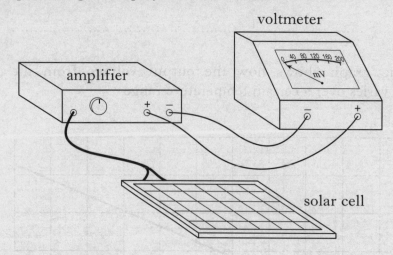

(a) Enter the names of each of the three parts of this electronic system in the block diagram below.

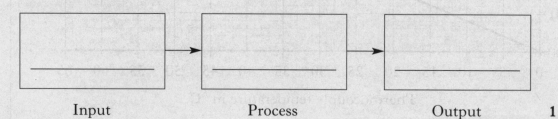

Input   Process   Output   **1**

(b) The table shows the voltage generated by the solar cell, and the output voltage of the amplifier for various values of light level. (Light level is measured in lux.)

Light level (lux)	350	400	450	500	550
Voltage generated by solar cell (mV)	0·1	0·2	0·3	0·4	0·5
Output voltage of amplifier (mV)	40	80	120	160	200

    (i) Calculate the voltage gain of the amplifier.

Space for working and answer

2

Marks | K&U | PS

7. (*b*) **(continued)**

(ii) The solar cell is connected to the amplifier as shown.

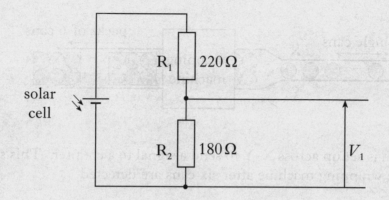

solar
cell

R$_1$ 220 Ω

R$_2$ 180 Ω

V_1

Calculate the voltage V_1 when the solar cell is in a light level of
500 lux.

Space for working and answer

$$V_2 = \left(\frac{R_2}{R_1 + R_2}\right) V_S$$

$$\left(\frac{180}{220 + 180}\right) 0.4$$

3

[Turn over

Marks | K&U | PS

8. A factory wraps cans in packs of six. The cans travel in a single line along a conveyor belt to a wrapping machine which seals them in plastic.

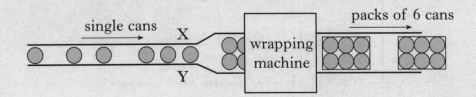

A light beam is set up across X–Y to send a signal to a counter. This signal operates the wrapping machine after six cans are detected.

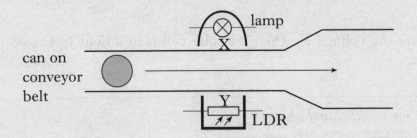

(*a*) The circuit shown produces the input signal for the counter.

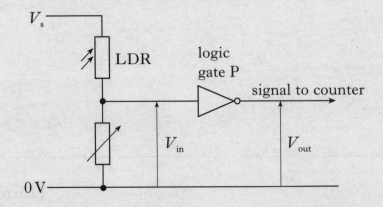

(i) What type of logic gate is P?

1

Marks | K&U | PS

8. (*a*) **(continued)**

(ii) Complete the following table, writing either **high** or **low** for each entry, to show what happens as cans pass through the light beam.

	No can in light beam	*Can in light beam*
Light level at LDR		
Resistance of LDR		
V_{in}		
V_{out}		

4

(*b*) The output of gate P goes to the counter. A 7-segment display shows the number of cans at the wrapping machine. Part of this circuit is shown below.

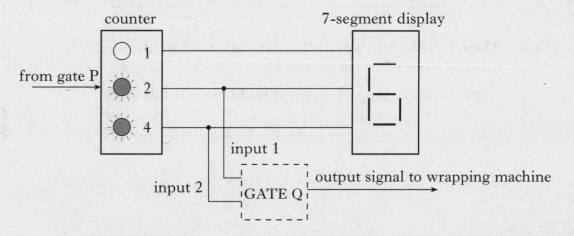

(i) Complete each sentence below by choosing a word from the following list.

analogue   binary   decimal

The output of the counter circuit is ....

The output of the 7-segment display is..................................... 2

[Turn over

8. (b) (continued)

(ii) Gate Q sends a signal to the wrapping machine when six cans have been detected.

(A) What type of logic gate is Q?

.... 1

(B) Complete the truth table for gate Q.

Input 1	Input 2	Output
0	0	
0	1	
1	0	
1	1	

2

(iii) There is a short delay to allow six cans to enter the wrapping machine before they are wrapped.

Name a suitable input device that could provide this delay.

.... 1

Marks | K&U | PS

9. On one road the speed limit is 90 km/h.

   (*a*) Show by calculation that this speed limit is 25 m/s.

Space for working and answer

2

   (*b*) A speed camera is used to detect motorists breaking the speed limit on this road. A section of the road in view of the camera is marked out with white lines spaced 2 m apart.

 speed camera

white lines on road

→ 2 m ←

The camera unit is fitted with a radar speed sensor. When a passing vehicle breaks the speed limit, the camera takes a pair of photographs 0·4 s apart.

When the speed camera film is later analysed, the following pair of photographs is obtained.

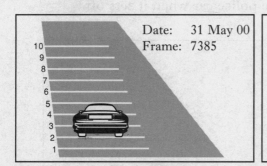 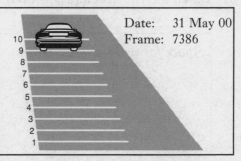

Calculate how much **faster** than the speed limit of 25 m/s this car was travelling.

Space for working and answer

3

9. (continued)

(c) Further along the road, a sports car travelling at a constant speed of 40 m/s passes a police car which is parked in a lay-by. The police car follows the sports car.

The speed-time graph shows the motion of both cars from the time the sports car passes the parked police car.

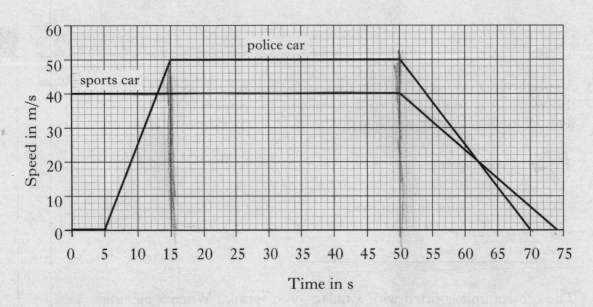

(i) How long does it take for the police car to start to move?

....

1

(ii) Calculate the acceleration of the police car when it sets off.

Space for working and answer

2

DO NOT WRITE IN THIS MARGIN

Marks | K&U | PS

9. (c) (continued)

(iii) Fifty seconds (50 s) after being passed by the sports car, the police car has travelled 2000 m.

Show by calculation that the cars are side by side at this time.

Space for working and answer

2

(iv) By calculating the distance travelled by each car while decelerating, show which car stops in front **and** the distance between them when both cars are stopped.

Space for working and answer

3

[Turn over

Marks | K&U | PS

10. An electric storage heater contains a heating element, thermal blocks and insulation as shown in the diagram.

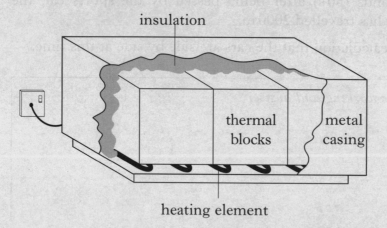

insulation

thermal
blocks

metal
casing

heating element

The heating element heats the thermal blocks during the night.

(a) Between midnight and 6.00 am, 8.64×10^7 J of energy are supplied to the heating element.

   (i) Calculate the power rating of the heating element.

   Space for working and answer

   2

   (ii) The total mass of the thermal blocks in the heater is 144 kg and the specific heat capacity of the thermal blocks is 2625 J/kg°C.

   Calculate the maximum possible rise in the temperature of the thermal blocks between midnight and 6.00 am.

   Space for working and answer

   2

Marks | K&U | PS

10. **(*a*)** **(continued)**

(iii) Explain why the actual temperature rise of the blocks is less than the value calculated in (*a*)(ii).

....

.... 1

(*b*) Why is there insulation between the thermal blocks and the outer casing of the heater?

....

....

.... 1

(*c*) During the day, heat energy stored in the heater is released into the room. State **one** way in which heat is transferred to the surroundings from this heater.

....

.... 1

[Turn over

Marks | K&U | PS

11. A refracting telescope has an objective lens which has a focal length of 800 mm and a diameter of 50 mm.

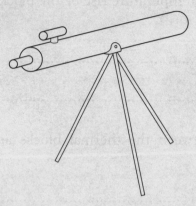

The telescope can be fitted with any one of three eyepiece lenses Q, R or S. Information on these lenses is shown in the table.

Lens	Focal length (mm)	Diameter (mm)
Q	10	5
R	20	5
S	40	5

(a) Why is it important to make the diameter of the **objective** lens as large as possible?

....

.... 1

Marks | K&U | PS

11. (continued)

(b) (i) Calculate the power of lens R.

> *Space for working and answer*

2

(ii) Which of the three eyepiece lenses has the greatest power?

.... 1

(c) Each eyepiece lens can be used on its own as a magnifying glass.

Complete the diagram below to show how lens S can be used to form a magnified image of an object.

The points marked F are one focal length from the centre of the lens.

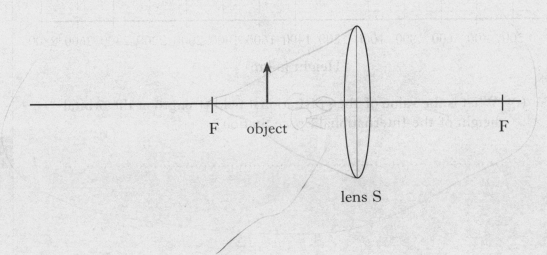

lens S

3

Marks | K&U | PS

12. The International Space Station orbits Earth at a height of 360 km. The command module of the space station has a mass of 20 tonnes (20×10^3 kg).

(*a*) Masses as large as this are difficult to accelerate.

Circle the term that is used for this concept.

gravitational field strength   inertia   thrust   weight   1

(*b*) The graph shows how the gravitational field strength varies with height above the surface of the Earth.

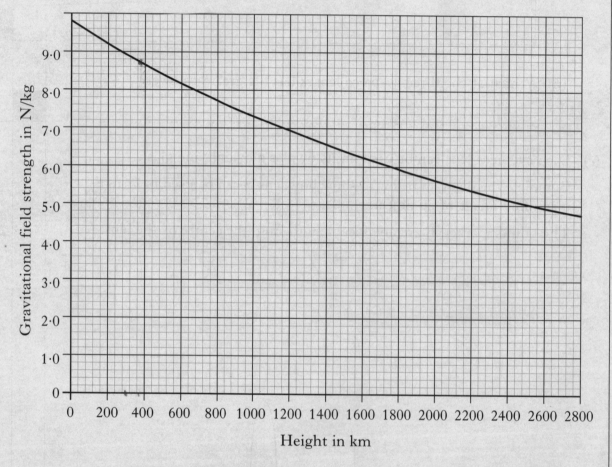

(i) What is the value of the gravitational field strength at the orbital height of the International Space Station?

....   1

Marks | K&U | PS

12. **(b) (continued)**

(ii) Calculate the weight of the command module at this height.

Space for working and answer

2

(iii) As the command module is taken from Earth to its orbital height, what happens to its weight and mass?

Weight ....

Mass 2

(c) The International Space Station is an artificial satellite.

Explain why it remains in orbit around the Earth.

....

....

....

.... 2

[END OF QUESTION PAPER]

K&U	PS

YOU MAY USE THE SPACE ON THIS PAGE TO REWRITE ANY ANSWER YOU HAVE DECIDED TO CHANGE IN THE MAIN PART OF THE ANSWER BOOKLET. TAKE CARE TO WRITE IN CAREFULLY THE APPROPRIATE QUESTION NUMBER.

FOR OFFICIAL USE

C

K & U	PS

Total Marks

3220/402

NATIONAL
QUALIFICATIONS
2001

MONDAY, 4 JUNE
10.50 AM – 12.35 PM

PHYSICS
STANDARD GRADE
Credit Level

Fill in these boxes and read what is printed below.

Full name of centre

Town

Forename(s)

Surname

Date of birth
Day Month Year

Scottish candidate number

Number of seat

1 All questions should be answered.

2 The questions may be answered in any order but all answers must be written clearly and legibly in this book.

3 Write your answer where indicated by the question or in the space provided after the question.

4 If you change your mind about your answer you may score it out and rewrite it in the space provided at the end of the answer book.

5 Before leaving the examination room you must give this book to the invigilator. If you do not, you may lose all the marks for this paper.

6 Any necessary data will be found in the **data sheet** on page two.

SCOTTISH
QUALIFICATIONS
AUTHORITY

DATA SHEET

Speed of light in materials

Material	Speed in m/s
Air	$3 \cdot 0 \times 10^8$
Carbon dioxide	$3 \cdot 0 \times 10^8$
Diamond	$1 \cdot 2 \times 10^8$
Glass	$2 \cdot 0 \times 10^8$
Glycerol	$2 \cdot 1 \times 10^8$
Water	$2 \cdot 3 \times 10^8$

Speed of sound in materials

Material	Speed in m/s
Aluminium	5200
Air	340
Bone	4100
Carbon dioxide	270
Glycerol	1900
Muscle	1600
Steel	5200
Tissue	1500
Water	1500

Gravitational field strengths

	Gravitational field strength on the surface in N/kg
Earth	10
Jupiter	26
Mars	4
Mercury	4
Moon	$1 \cdot 6$
Neptune	12
Saturn	11
Sun	270
Venus	9

Specific heat capacity of materials

Material	Specific heat capacity in J/kg °C
Alcohol	2350
Aluminium	902
Copper	386
Diamond	530
Glass	500
Glycerol	2400
Ice	2100
Lead	128
Water	4180

Specific latent heat of fusion of materials

Material	Specific latent heat of fusion in J/kg
Alcohol	$0 \cdot 99 \times 10^5$
Aluminium	$3 \cdot 95 \times 10^5$
Carbon dioxide	$1 \cdot 80 \times 10^5$
Copper	$2 \cdot 05 \times 10^5$
Glycerol	$1 \cdot 81 \times 10^5$
Lead	$0 \cdot 25 \times 10^5$
Water	$3 \cdot 34 \times 10^5$

Melting and boiling points of materials

Material	Melting point in °C	Boiling point in °C
Alcohol	−98	65
Aluminium	660	2470
Copper	1077	2567
Glycerol	18	290
Lead	328	1737
Turpentine	−10	156

Specific latent heat of vaporisation of materials

Material	Specific latent heat of vaporisation in J/kg
Alcohol	$11 \cdot 2 \times 10^5$
Carbon dioxide	$3 \cdot 77 \times 10^5$
Glycerol	$8 \cdot 30 \times 10^5$
Turpentine	$2 \cdot 90 \times 10^5$
Water	$22 \cdot 6 \times 10^5$

SI Prefixes and Multiplication Factors

Prefix	Symbol	Factor	
giga	G	1 000 000 000	$= 10^9$
mega	M	1 000 000	$= 10^6$
kilo	k	1000	$= 10^3$
milli	m	0·001	$= 10^{-3}$
micro	μ	0·000 001	$= 10^{-6}$
nano	n	0·000 000 001	$= 10^{-9}$

Marks | K&U | PS

1. The depth of the seabed is measured using pulses of ultrasound waves. The ultrasound waves are transmitted from a stationary ship. The waves are reflected from the seabed as shown and are detected by equipment on the ship. The transmitted ultrasound waves have a frequency of 30 kHz.

transmitted pulse

reflected pulse   seabed

(a) One pulse of ultrasound waves is received back at the ship 0·2 s after being sent out.

(i) Use the data sheet to find the speed of the ultrasound waves in the water.

....   1

(ii) Calculate the depth of the seabed.

Space for working and answer

3

(iii) Calculate the wavelength of the ultrasound waves in the water.

Space for working and answer

2

[Turn over

1. (continued)

(b) The ultrasound waves lose energy as they travel through the water. The transmitted wave is displayed on an oscilloscope screen as shown.

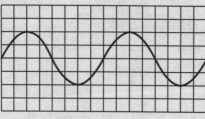

Transmitted

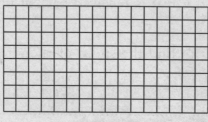

Reflected

On the bottom part of the diagram, sketch the trace produced by the reflected wave.

2

(c) The frequency of the transmitted wave is increased to 60 kHz.

What happens to the time interval between the transmitted pulse and the reflected pulse?

Explain your answer.

....

....

....

.... **2**

Page four

DO NOT WRITE IN THIS MARGIN

Marks	K&U	PS

2. A mobile phone has a power of 75 mW and operates using a 3 V battery.

(*a*) Calculate the current taken from the battery when the mobile phone is being used.

Space for working and answer

2

(*b*) Which of the following fuses should be connected in series with the battery of the mobile phone?

20 mA **100 mA** **2 A** **3 A**

.... 1

[Turn over

Marks | K&U | PS

3. A 2·5 V, 100 mA lamp is operated at its correct power rating from a 12 V battery by using the circuit shown.

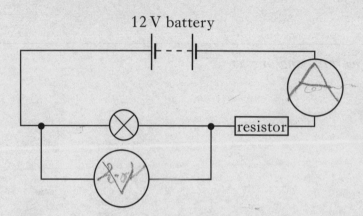

(*a*) A voltmeter and an ammeter included in the circuit show that the lamp is operating at its correct rating.

Enter the readings that are seen on the meters. Include the units for both readings.

2

(*b*) (i) Calculate the voltage across the resistor.

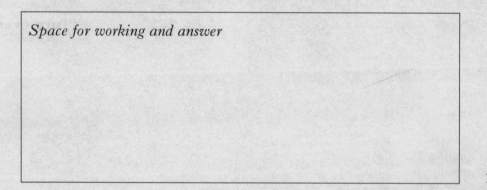

Space for working and answer

1

(ii) Calculate the resistance of the resistor.

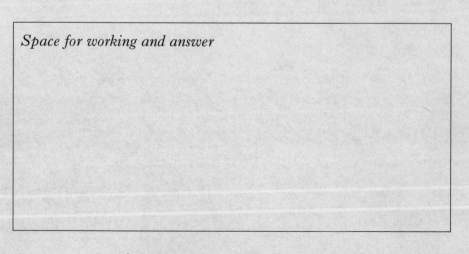

Space for working and answer

2

Marks | K&U | PS

4. A simple d.c. motor is shown in Figure 1.

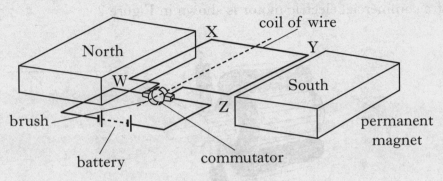

Figure 1

(a) The coil WXYZ rotates in a clockwise direction.

State **two** changes that could be made to make the coil rotate in the opposite direction.

Change 1 ....

....

Change 2 ....

.... 2

[Turn over

DO NOT WRITE IN THIS MARGIN

Marks	K&U	PS

4. (continued)

(*b*) Part of a commercial electric motor is shown in Figure 2.

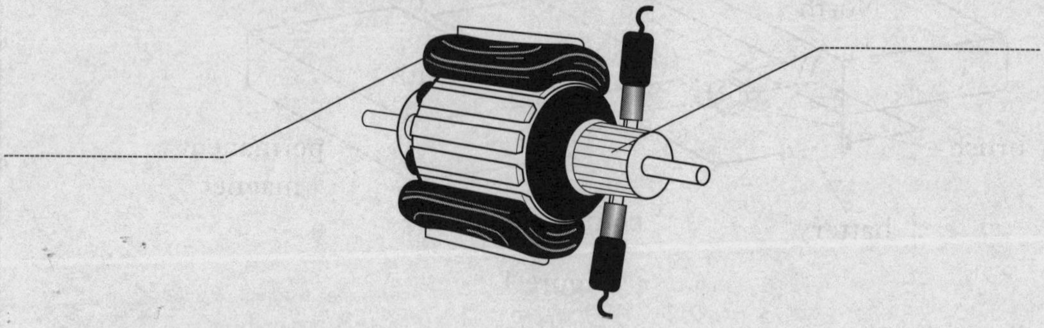

Figure 2

(i) Label the two parts indicated on the motor, using names from the list below.

brush **commutator** **field coil** **rotating coil** 2

(ii) In the commercial electric motor, state why

(A) more than one rotating coil is used

....

.... 1

(B) field coils rather than permanent magnets are used.

....

.... 1

Marks | K&U | PS

5. (a) A long-sighted person is prescribed glasses that have lenses each with a power of 2·5 D.

    (i) State what is meant by long-sight.

....

....

        1

    (ii) Calculate the focal length of each lens.

Space for working and answer

        2

(b) Complete the diagram below to show the path of the ray of light after it emerges from the lens.

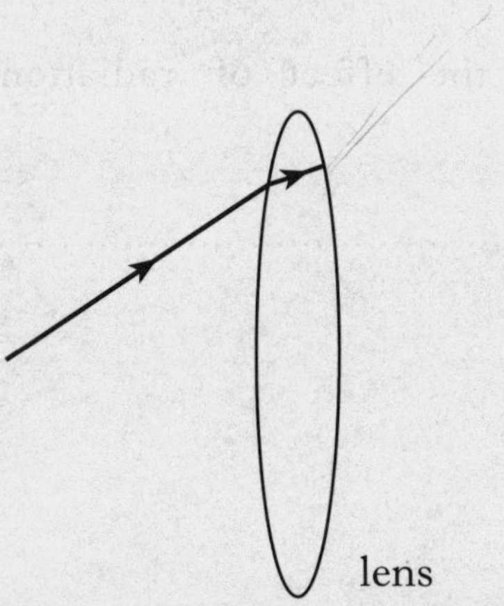

lens

        1

[Turn over

Marks | K&U | PS

6. Carbon dating is used by scientists to tell the age of organic (formerly living) material. This method is based on knowing that the half-life of radioactive carbon is 5730 years.

(a) Explain what is meant by the statement "the half-life of radioactive carbon is 5730 years".

....

.... **2**

(b) The proportion of radioactive carbon in the organic material is found by measuring its activity using a scintillation counter.

(i) State the **unit** that is used for the activity of a radioactive source.

.... **1**

(ii) Describe how a scintillation counter is used as a detector of radiation.

....

....

.... **2**

(iii) State an example of the effect of radiation other than scintillations.

.... **1**

Marks | K&U | PS

7. A thermistor is used as a temperature sensor in the voltage divider circuit shown below. The circuit is used to sense the temperature of water in a tank. When the temperature of the water in the tank falls below a certain value, the output of the voltage divider causes a switching circuit to operate a heater.

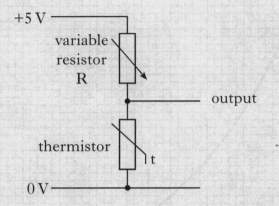

(a) When the voltage across the thermistor reaches 0·7 V, the circuit causes the heater to be switched on.

   (i) The variable resistor R is set to a resistance of 4300 Ω.

      Calculate the resistance of the thermistor when the voltage across the thermistor is 0·7 V.

> *Space for working and answer*

2

[Turn over

Marks | K&U | PS

7. **(a)** **(continued)**

(ii) The graph shows how the resistance of the thermistor changes with temperature.

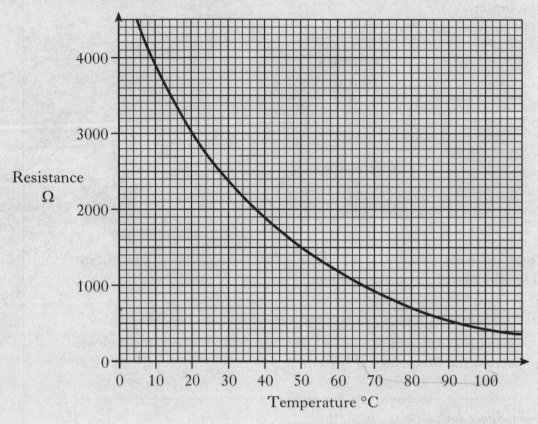

(A) Use the graph to decide the temperature at which the heater is switched on.

.... 1

(B) The resistance of the variable resistor R is increased to a value **greater than** $4300\,\Omega$.

What effect does this have on the temperature at which the heater is switched on?

Explain your answer.

....

....

.... 2

7. (continued)

(b) The voltage divider circuit is connected to the switching circuit, as shown, to operate the heater. When there is a current in the relay coil, the relay switch closes.

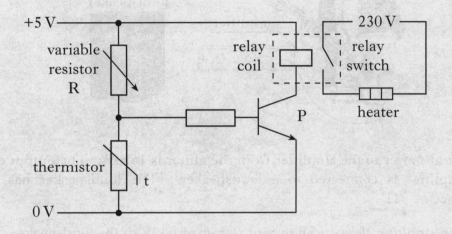

(i) Name component P.

.... **1**

(ii) Explain why the heater switches on as the temperature falls below a selected value.

....

....

....

....

.... **3**

[Turn over

Marks | K&U | PS

8. An electric guitar is connected to an amplifier.

The input power to the amplifier from the guitar is 16 mW. The output of the amplifier is connected to a loudspeaker. The loudspeaker has a resistance of 9 Ω.

(a) The amplifier delivers an output power of 64 W to the loudspeaker.

(i) Calculate the power gain of the amplifier.

Space for working and answer

2

(ii) Calculate the voltage across the loudspeaker.

Space for working and answer

2

DO NOT WRITE IN THIS MARGIN

Marks | K&U | PS

8. (continued)

(*b*) A second, identical loudspeaker is connected in parallel with the first.

Calculate the combined resistance of the two loudspeakers in parallel.

Space for working and answer

2

(*c*) The guitarist plays a note of frequency 256 Hz.

What is the frequency of the output signal from the amplifier?

.... 1

[Turn over

Marks | K&U | PS

9. A cyclist has a small computer attached to her bike. The computer gives information on the cyclist's instantaneous speed, distance travelled and time taken.

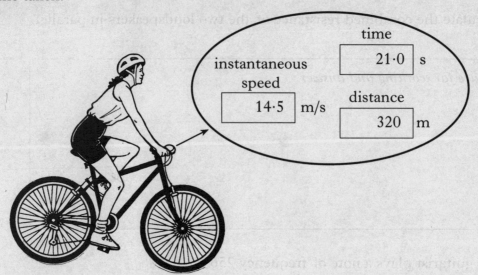

time
21·0 s

instantaneous
speed
14·5 m/s

distance
320 m

At a point during a journey, the readings on the display are as shown above.

(a) (i) Calculate the average speed of the cyclist up to this point.

(You must use an appropriate number of significant figures in your answer to this question.)

Space for working and answer

3

(ii) Why is the average speed of the cyclist not always the same as the instantaneous speed displayed on the computer?

....

....

.... 2

DO NOT WRITE IN THIS MARGIN

Marks K&U PS

9. (continued)

(*b*) (i) The total mass of the cyclist and bike is 80 kg.

Calculate the total kinetic energy of the cyclist and the bike at this point during the journey.

Space for working and answer

2

(ii) The cyclist brakes to a halt in a distance of 50 m.

Calculate the braking force used.

Space for working and answer

2

[Turn over

DO NOT WRITE IN THIS MARGIN

Marks | K&U | PS

10. An aircraft has a mass of 268 000 kg. The aircraft accelerates from rest along a straight runway. It takes 40 s for the aircraft to reach its take-off speed of 80 m/s.

(a) The speed-time graph of the aircraft is shown.

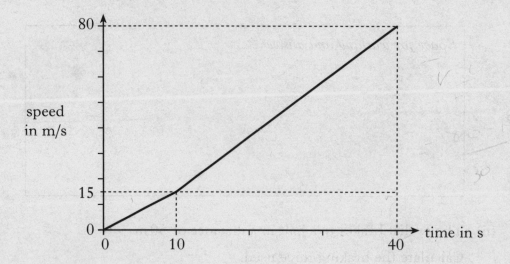

(i) Calculate the acceleration of the aircraft **during the first 10 s**.

Space for working and answer

2

(ii) Calculate the unbalanced force acting on the aircraft **during the first 10 s**.

Space for working and answer

2

Official SQA Past Papers: Credit Physics 2001

DO NOT
WRITE IN
THIS
MARGIN

Marks K&U PS

10. (a) (continued)

(iii) By using information **from the graph**, explain whether the unbalanced force on the aircraft is greater during the time period 0–10 s or 10 s–40 s.

....

....

....

2

(iv) Calculate the length of runway required to allow the aircraft to reach its take-off speed.

Space for working and answer

3

(b) After take-off, the aircraft flies at a constant height of 10 000 m. The pilot increases the speed of the aircraft at this height.

The diagram shows the forces acting on the aircraft at this height.

lift (upwards force)

engine thrust

air friction force

weight

Complete the statements about the sizes of the forces acting on the aircraft by using phrases from the following list.

equal to   greater than   less than

(i) The engine thrust is.................................... the air friction force.   1

(ii) The lift is....................................... the weight.   1

Marks | K&U | PS

11. (a) The following information relates to two power stations, a fossil fuel power station and a nuclear power station.

Fossil Fuel Power Station	Nuclear Power Station
Heat energy produced per kilogram of fuel $\quad 4\cdot5 \times 10^7\,$J	Heat energy produced per kilogram of fuel $\quad 4\cdot4 \times 10^{11}\,$J
Waste produced per year —not radioactive $\qquad 100\,000\,$kg	Waste produced per year —radioactive $\qquad 5\,$kg
Cooling water required $\qquad 550\,$kg/s	Cooling water required $\qquad 550\,$kg/s

(i) Compare the information given for the two types of power station. State **one** advantage of generating electricity using each type of power station.

Fossil fuel ....

....

Nuclear..

.... 2

(ii) Using information given, state where both types of power station are likely to be located.

Explain why they are built in these locations.

....

....

.... 2

(b) A simple block diagram of a nuclear power station is shown below.

| Reactor core | → | Turbine | → | Generator |

State the energy transformation that takes place in

(i) the reactor core

.... 1

(ii) the generator.

.... 1

Marks | K&U | PS

11. **(continued)**

(*c*) The diagram shows what happens when a uranium nucleus undergoes fission in a nuclear reaction.

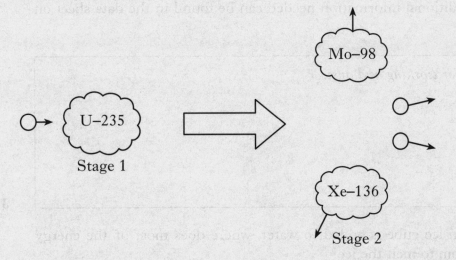

(i) Circle **one** word in each set of brackets to describe what happens at each stage.

Stage 1: A uranium nucleus is bombarded by a $\begin{Bmatrix} \text{proton} \\ \text{neutron} \\ \text{electron} \end{Bmatrix}$.

Stage 2: The uranium nucleus disintegrates, producing fission

fragments, two $\begin{Bmatrix} \text{protons} \\ \text{neutrons} \\ \text{electrons} \end{Bmatrix}$ and $\begin{Bmatrix} \text{plutonium} \\ \text{heat} \\ \text{electricity} \end{Bmatrix}$.

3

(ii) Describe how, in a nuclear reactor, the above process can result in a chain reaction.

....

....

.... 3

[Turn over

Marks | K&U | PS

12. Ice cubes are used to cool down water for drinking. Each ice cube has a mass of 12 g and is initially at a temperature of 0 °C.

(a) Calculate how much heat is needed to melt an ice cube.

(Any additional information needed can be found in the data sheet on page 2.)

> Space for working and answer

3

(b) When an ice cube is added to water, where does most of the energy come from to melt the ice?

....

1

(c) (i) An ice cube is added to a glass containing 200 g of water.

The initial temperature of the water is 18 °C. The final temperature when all of the ice has melted is 15 °C.

Calculate the heat removed from the water.

(Any additional information needed can be found in the data sheet on page 2.)

> Space for working and answer

3

(ii) Suggest a final temperature when an ice cube is added to an insulated bottle of water. The bottle has a lid and contains an equal mass of water as above, and is at the same initial temperature.

Explain your answer.

....

....

....

2

Marks K&U PS

13. Read the following passage about the launching of a space observatory using the Space Shuttle Columbia:

In July 1999, NASA used the Space Shuttle Columbia to launch a space-based observatory, called the Chandra X-ray Observatory.

This observatory is designed to detect X-rays emitted by objects in our solar system and beyond. X-rays are absorbed by the Earth's atmosphere, so a space-based observatory is necessary to detect them. Signals are sent from the observatory to Earth using radio waves.

There are now three observatories orbiting the Earth. The other two are the Hubble Space Telescope that detects visible light and the Compton Gamma Ray Observatory.

(*a*) Why is it necessary to site an observatory in space to detect X-rays?

....

.... 1

(*b*) Four members of the electromagnetic spectrum are mentioned in the passage. Complete the diagram by placing these members in the correct order of wavelength.

		Ultraviolet		Infrared	Microwaves	

The electromagnetic spectrum 4

(*c*) Explain why different kinds of observatory are used to detect signals from space.

....

....

.... 2

[Turn over

Official SQA Past Papers: Credit Physics 2001

DO NOT
WRITE IN
THIS
MARGIN

Marks | K&U | PS

13. (continued)

(*d*) When the Space Shuttle reached the correct height above Earth, the observatory was separated from it.

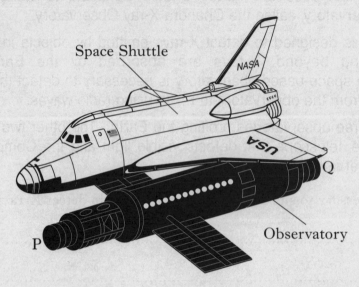

Space Shuttle

Observatory

P   Q

Two rocket motors P and Q on the observatory, as shown, were used during the separation. The observatory accelerated away from the space shuttle for a short time. It then remained at a fixed distance ahead of the space shuttle. Describe how the rockets P and Q were used during this separation.

....

....

....

....   2

[END OF QUESTION PAPER]

2002 CREDIT

C

FOR OFFICIAL USE

K & U	PS

Total Marks

3220/402

NATIONAL
QUALIFICATIONS
2002

MONDAY, 27 MAY
10.50 AM – 12.35 PM

PHYSICS
STANDARD GRADE
Credit Level

Fill in these boxes and read what is printed below.

Full name of centre

Town

Forename(s)

Surname

Date of birth
Day Month Year

Scottish candidate number

Number of seat

1 All questions should be answered.

2 The questions may be answered in any order but all answers must be written clearly and legibly in this book.

3 Write your answer where indicated by the question or in the space provided after the question.

4 If you change your mind about your answer you may score it out and rewrite it in the space provided at the end of the answer book.

5 Before leaving the examination room you must give this book to the invigilator. If you do not, you may lose all the marks for this paper.

6 Any necessary data will be found in the **data sheet** on page two.

SCOTTISH
QUALIFICATIONS
AUTHORITY

Speed of light in materials

Material	Speed in m/s
Air	$3 \cdot 0 \times 10^8$
Carbon dioxide	$3 \cdot 0 \times 10^8$
Diamond	$1 \cdot 2 \times 10^8$
Glass	$2 \cdot 0 \times 10^8$
Glycerol	$2 \cdot 1 \times 10^8$
Water	$2 \cdot 3 \times 10^8$

Speed of sound in materials

Material	Speed in m/s
Aluminium	5200
Air	340
Bone	4100
Carbon dioxide	270
Glycerol	1900
Muscle	1600
Steel	5200
Tissue	1500
Water	1500

Gravitational field strengths

	Gravitational field strength on the surface in N/kg
Earth	10
Jupiter	26
Mars	4
Mercury	4
Moon	$1 \cdot 6$
Neptune	12
Saturn	11
Sun	270
Venus	9

Specific heat capacity of materials

Material	Specific heat capacity in J/kg °C
Alcohol	2350
Aluminium	902
Copper	386
Diamond	530
Glass	500
Glycerol	2400
Ice	2100
Lead	128
Water	4180

Specific latent heat of fusion of materials

Material	Specific latent heat of fusion in J/kg
Alcohol	$0 \cdot 99 \times 10^5$
Aluminium	$3 \cdot 95 \times 10^5$
Carbon dioxide	$1 \cdot 80 \times 10^5$
Copper	$2 \cdot 05 \times 10^5$
Glycerol	$1 \cdot 81 \times 10^5$
Lead	$0 \cdot 25 \times 10^5$
Water	$3 \cdot 34 \times 10^5$

Melting and boiling points of materials

Material	Melting point in °C	Boiling point in °C
Alcohol	−98	65
Aluminium	660	2470
Copper	1077	2567
Glycerol	18	290
Lead	328	1737
Turpentine	−10	156

Specific latent heat of vaporisation of materials

Material	Specific latent heat of vaporisation in J/kg
Alcohol	$11 \cdot 2 \times 10^5$
Carbon dioxide	$3 \cdot 77 \times 10^5$
Glycerol	$8 \cdot 30 \times 10^5$
Turpentine	$2 \cdot 90 \times 10^5$
Water	$22 \cdot 6 \times 10^5$

SI Prefixes and Multiplication Factors

Prefix	Symbol	Factor	
giga	G	1 000 000 000	$= 10^9$
mega	M	1 000 000	$= 10^6$
kilo	k	1000	$= 10^3$
milli	m	0·001	$= 10^{-3}$
micro	μ	0·000 001	$= 10^{-6}$
nano	n	0·000 000 001	$= 10^{-9}$

1. Radio Alba transmits on a range of frequencies from different transmitters throughout Scotland.

On a car journey from Aberdeen to Stirling a driver listens to Radio Alba. At the start of the journey she tunes to the signal transmitted from transmitter P.

(a) Complete the following passage, using some of the words from the list below. Do not use any word more than once.

amplitude	**audio**	**carrier**
frequency	**modulation**	**radio**

The transmitter transmits a................................signal, which consists

of an ....wave and a................................wave. The

process of combining these waves is known as **2**

(b) During the journey the driver finds that the signal from transmitter P fades.

(i) Suggest a reason why the signal fades.

....

....   **1**

(ii) To continue to listen to Radio Alba, the driver re-tunes the radio to pick up the signal from transmitter Q.

What is the difference between the carrier wave from transmitter P and that from transmitter Q?

....

....   **1**

Marks | K&U | PS

2. The table gives information about artificial satellites that orbit the Earth.

Name of satellite	Period (minutes)	Height above Earth (km)	Use
Landsat	99	705	Land mapping
ERS-1		780	Monitoring sea levels
NOAA-12	102	833	Distribution of ozone layer
Early Bird	1440	35 900	Continuous telecommunication

(a) NOAA-12 uses radio waves to transmit signals relating to the ozone layer.

  (i) What is the speed of radio waves?

  .... **1**

  (ii) Calculate the time for signals to travel from NOAA-12 to an Earth station immediately below the satellite.

  Space for working and answer

  2

  (iii) Signals transmitted from NOAA-12 have a frequency of 137·5 MHz.

  Calculate the wavelength of these signals.

  Space for working and answer

  2

Marks | K&U | PS

2. (continued)

(b) Using information about the period of Early Bird, explain why this satellite is used for continuous telecommunication between two points on the Earth's surface.

....

....

.... **2**

(c) Give an approximate value, **in minutes**, for the period of orbit of ERS-1.

.... **1**

(d) Landsat monitors heat emission from the land to build up a thermographic image.

Which part of the electromagnetic spectrum is detected by Landsat?

.... **1**

(e) As well as artificial satellites, there is one natural satellite that orbits the Earth. Name this natural satellite.

.... **1**

[Turn over

Marks | K&U | PS

3. A student uses the circuit below in experiments to investigate how the voltage across different components varies when the current in the components is changed.

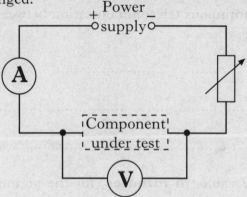

(a) The student places component X in the circuit and carries out an experiment. The graph below shows how the voltage across component X varies with current.

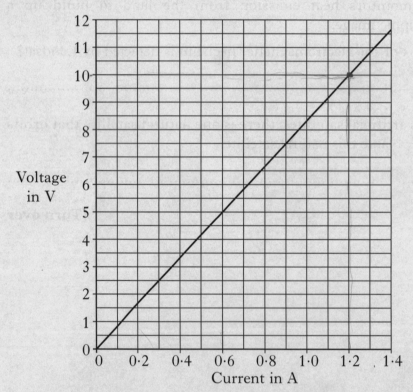

(i) Calculate the resistance of component X when the current is 1·2 A.

(You must use an appropriate number of significant figures in your answer to this question.)

```
Space for working and answer
```

[3220/402]   *Page six*

2

Marks | K&U | PS

3. (*a*) (**continued**)

(ii) Using information from the graph, explain what happens to the resistance of component X as the current is increased.

Justify your answer by calculation or otherwise.

.... | *Space for working*

....

....

....

....

....

3

(*b*) The student replaces component X with component Y, repeats the experiment and obtains the following graph.

(i) The student concludes that the resistance of component Y is not constant. Why is the student correct in coming to this conclusion?

....

....

1

[Turn over

Marks | K&U | PS

3. **(b)** **(continued)**

    (ii) (A) From the graph, what is the current in component Y when the voltage across component Y is 12 V?

.... **1**

        (B) Calculate the power dissipated in component Y when the voltage across it is 12 V.

> *Space for working and answer*

  2

4. The diagram shows three household circuits, connected to a consumer unit.

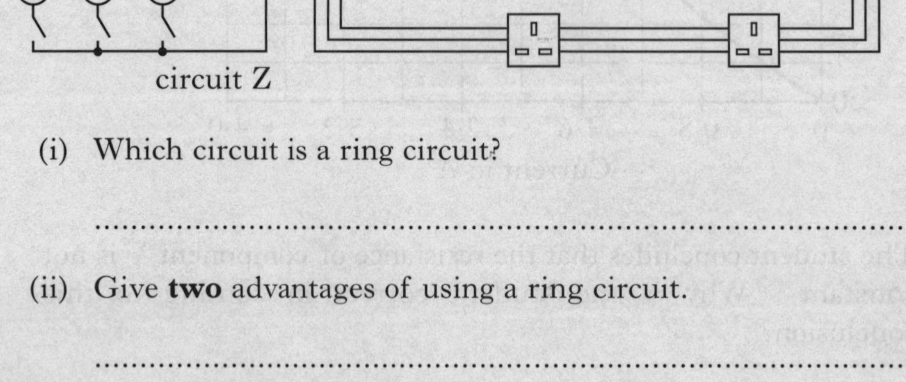

  (*a*) (i) Which circuit is a ring circuit?

.... **1**

      (ii) Give **two** advantages of using a ring circuit.

....

.... **2**

DO NOT
WRITE IN
THIS
MARGIN

Marks | K&U | PS

4. **(continued)**

(b) State and explain **one** difference between a lighting circuit and a ring circuit.

....

....

....

2

(c) (i) Why does a cooker need a separate circuit?

....

....

....

1

(ii) One heating element of the cooker has a power rating of 2·2 kW. Calculate how many joules of energy are transferred by this element in 2 hours.

Space for working and answer

2

(d) (i) What is the purpose of an earth wire?

....

....

1

(ii) Explain how an earth wire works.

....

....

....

2

[Turn over

Marks | K&U | PS

5. Ultrasound is used by doctors for treatment and diagnosis.

(a) Pulses of ultrasound are used to produce local heating of muscle deep inside the body. This heating effect can help relieve pain in the muscles.

(i) What is meant by ultrasound?

....

.... **1**

(ii) Calculate the time for a pulse of ultrasound to travel through 2 cm of muscle.

(Data you require will be found in the Data Sheet on *page two*.)

```
Space for working and answer
```

3

(b) Ultrasound is also used to build up images of an unborn baby.

(i) Explain how ultrasound is used to build up such images.

....

....

....

.... **2**

(ii) Why is ultrasound safer than X-rays for this sort of medical application?

....

.... **1**

Marks | K&U | PS

6. A student investigates the effect of glass shapes on rays of light.

(a) The student places glass shapes in the path of three rays of red light as shown.

(i) Complete the diagram to show the paths of the rays of light through and out of the three glass shapes.

3

(ii) The student has drawn line PQ on the diagram at shape X at right angles to the glass surface.

What name is given to this line?

....

1

(iii) **On the diagram**, label **one** angle of incidence as *i* and **one** angle of refraction as *r*.

2

(b) Name the type of lens that would have a similar effect on the rays of light as the three glass shapes, arranged as in part (a).

....

1

[Turn over

Marks | K&U | PS

7. The exit of an underground car park has an automatic barrier. The barrier rises when a car interrupts a light beam across the exit and money has been put into the pay machine. The barrier can also be operated by using a manual switch.

The light beam is directed at an LDR that is connected as shown in the circuit below.

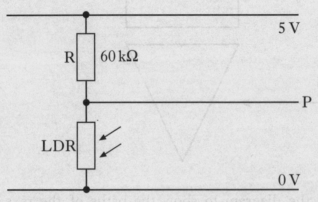

(a) Calculate the voltage across the LDR when its resistance is 15 kΩ.

Space for working and answer

2

Page twelve

Marks | K&U | PS

7. (continued)

(b) Part of the control circuit for the automatic barrier is shown below.

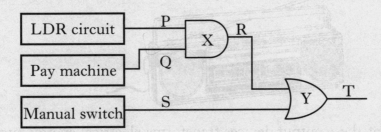

When a car interrupts the light beam, the logic level at P changes from logic 0 to logic 1.

When money is put into the pay machine, the logic level at Q changes from logic 0 to logic 1.

When the manual switch is operated, the logic level at S changes from logic 0 to logic 1.

(i) Name logic gate X.

.... 1

(ii) Name logic gate Y.

.... 1

(iii) Complete the truth table below for the control circuit shown, by filling in the values of the logic levels at R and T.

P	Q	R	S	T
0	0		0	
0	1		0	
1	0		0	
1	1		0	
0	0		1	
0	1		1	
1	0		1	
1	1		1	

4

(iv) Describe a situation where it would be necessary to operate the barrier by using the manual switch.

....

.... 1

[Turn over

DO NOT
WRITE IN
THIS
MARGIN

Marks | K&U | PS

8. A radio has three types of output device.

filament lamp   **LED**   **loudspeaker**

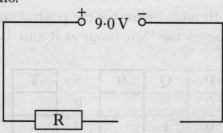

(a) Which of these output devices transforms electrical energy into sound energy?

.... 1

(b) Which of these output devices is most suitable for illuminating the front panel of the radio?

Explain your choice.

....

....

.... 2

(c) The LED is connected in series with resistor, R, to the 9·0 V power supply of the radio.

$$\overset{+}{\circ} \ 9{\cdot}0 \, V \ \overset{-}{\circ}$$

$$\boxed{R}$$

(i) In the space in the circuit above draw the LED connected correctly. 2

(ii) When lit, the voltage across the LED is 2·4 V and the current in the LED is 20 mA.

Calculate the resistance of R.

Space for working and answer

3

Marks | K&U | PS

9. A skateboarder is practising on a ramp. The total mass of the skateboarder and the board is 60 kg.

(a) Calculate the increase in potential energy of the skateboarder and board in moving from the ground to position P.

Space for working and answer

2

(b) The skateboarder moves along the ramp from P to R, and rises into the air above R.

  (i) At what point **on the ramp** is the kinetic energy of the skateboarder greatest?

  ....

1

  (ii) The vertical speed of the skateboarder at R is 6 m/s.

  Calculate the height that the skateboarder rises to, above R.

  Space for working and answer

3

  (iii) Explain why the skateboarder does not rise to the same height as P.

  ....

  ....

  ....

2

Marks | K&U | PS

10. At a greyhound racing track, the greyhounds are automatically released when an artificial hare crosses the starting line.

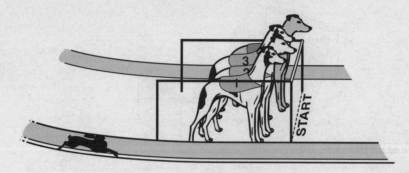

The speed-time graph shows the motion of one greyhound and the hare from the time when the hare crosses the starting line.

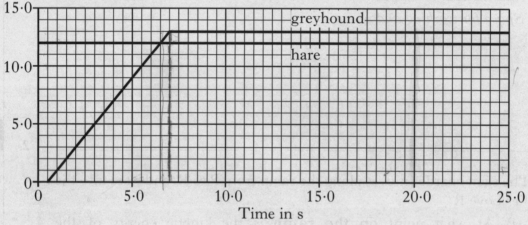

(a) How long does it take for the greyhound to start moving after the hare crosses the starting line?

.... 1

(b) Calculate the acceleration of the greyhound when it starts moving.

> *Space for working and answer*

2

DO NOT WRITE IN THIS MARGIN

Marks K&U PS

10. (continued)

(*c*) The hare crosses the finishing line 20 s after crossing the starting line.

(i) Over what distance is the race run?

Space for working and answer

2

(ii) How far behind the hare is the greyhound when the **hare** finishes the race?

Space for working and answer

3

[Turn over

Marks | K&U | PS

11. A lighting system in a shop window uses three identical 18 W, 12 V filament lamps. The lamps are operated at their correct rating from the 230 V mains supply using a transformer as shown below.

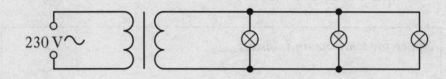

There are 5750 turns on the primary coil of the transformer.

(a) Calculate the number of turns on the secondary coil of the transformer.

> Space for working and answer

2

(b) (i) The current in each lamp is 1·5 A.

Calculate the total current in the secondary circuit of the transformer.

> Space for working and answer

1

(ii) Assuming that the transformer is 100% efficient, calculate the current in the primary coil.

> Space for working and answer

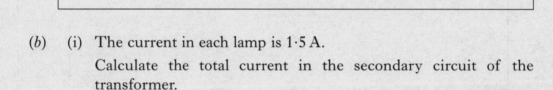

2

DO NOT WRITE IN THIS MARGIN

Marks | K&U | PS

11. (continued)

(*c*) (i) Show that the resistance of one of the filament lamps, when it is operating normally, is 8·0 Ω.

Space for working and answer

2

(ii) Calculate the combined resistance of the three lamps in parallel.

Space for working and answer

2

[Turn over

Marks | K&U | PS

12. A student sets up the apparatus shown to measure the specific heat capacity of an aluminium block.

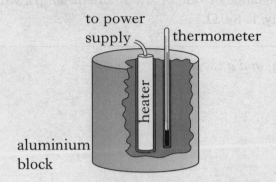

The student obtains the following results:

mass of aluminium block $m = 0.8\,\text{kg}$
temperature change $\Delta T = 19\,°\text{C}$
time taken $t = 5.0$ minutes
heater current $I = 4.2\,\text{A}$
heater voltage $V = 12\,\text{V}$

(a) Show, by calculation, that 15 120 J of electrical energy are supplied to the heater in 5·0 minutes.

> *Space for working and answer*

2

(b) (i) Assuming all of the electrical energy is transferred to the aluminium block as heat energy, calculate the value of the specific heat capacity of aluminium obtained from this experiment.

> *Space for working and answer*

2

Marks | K&U | PS

12. **(b)** **(continued)**

(ii) The accepted value of the specific heat capacity of aluminium is 902 J/kg °C.

(A) Give a reason for the difference between your answer in (b)(i) and this value.

....

....

.... **1**

(B) How could the experiment be improved to reduce this difference?

....

....

.... **1**

[Turn over

Marks | K&U | PS

13. During the Apollo 11 expedition to the Moon, 21 kg of soil samples were brought from the Moon to the Earth. The gravitational field strength was not constant throughout the journey.

(a) What is meant by gravitational field strength?

....

.... **1**

(b) Complete the table to show the mass and weight of the soil samples at various stages of the journey.

Stage	Gravitational field strength (N/kg)	Mass (kg)	Weight (N)
on the Moon	1·6	21	
at a point during the journey	0		
on the Earth	10		

3

[END OF QUESTION PAPER]

2003 CREDIT

FOR OFFICIAL USE

C

K & U	PS

Total Marks

3220/402

NATIONAL
QUALIFICATIONS
2003

MONDAY, 19 MAY
10.50 AM – 12.35 PM

PHYSICS
STANDARD GRADE
Credit Level

Fill in these boxes and read what is printed below.

Full name of centre

Town

Forename(s)

Surname

Date of birth
Day Month Year

Scottish candidate number

Number of seat

1 All questions should be answered.

2 The questions may be answered in any order but all answers must be written clearly and legibly in this book.

3 Write your answer where indicated by the question or in the space provided after the question.

4 If you change your mind about your answer you may score it out and rewrite it in the space provided at the end of the answer book.

5 Before leaving the examination room you must give this book to the invigilator. If you do not, you may lose all the marks for this paper.

6 Any necessary data will be found in the **data sheet** on page two.

SCOTTISH
QUALIFICATIONS
AUTHORITY

SAB 3220/402
6/3/3/25870

Speed of light in materials

Material	Speed in m/s
Air	$3 \cdot 0 \times 10^8$
Carbon dioxide	$3 \cdot 0 \times 10^8$
Diamond	$1 \cdot 2 \times 10^8$
Glass	$2 \cdot 0 \times 10^8$
Glycerol	$2 \cdot 1 \times 10^8$
Water	$2 \cdot 3 \times 10^8$

Speed of sound in materials

Material	Speed in m/s
Aluminium	5200
Air	340
Bone	4100
Carbon dioxide	270
Glycerol	1900
Muscle	1600
Steel	5200
Tissue	1500
Water	1500

Gravitational field strengths

	Gravitational field strength on the surface in N/kg
Earth	10
Jupiter	26
Mars	4
Mercury	4
Moon	$1 \cdot 6$
Neptune	12
Saturn	11
Sun	270
Venus	9

Specific heat capacity of materials

Material	Specific heat capacity in J/kg °C
Alcohol	2350
Aluminium	902
Copper	386
Diamond	530
Glass	500
Glycerol	2400
Ice	2100
Lead	128
Water	4180

Specific latent heat of fusion of materials

Material	Specific latent heat of fusion in J/kg
Alcohol	$0 \cdot 99 \times 10^5$
Aluminium	$3 \cdot 95 \times 10^5$
Carbon dioxide	$1 \cdot 80 \times 10^5$
Copper	$2 \cdot 05 \times 10^5$
Glycerol	$1 \cdot 81 \times 10^5$
Lead	$0 \cdot 25 \times 10^5$
Water	$3 \cdot 34 \times 10^5$

Melting and boiling points of materials

Material	Melting point in °C	Boiling point in °C
Alcohol	−98	65
Aluminium	660	2470
Copper	1077	2567
Glycerol	18	290
Lead	328	1737
Turpentine	−10	156

Specific latent heat of vaporisation of materials

Material	Specific latent heat of vaporisation in J/kg
Alcohol	$11 \cdot 2 \times 10^5$
Carbon dioxide	$3 \cdot 77 \times 10^5$
Glycerol	$8 \cdot 30 \times 10^5$
Turpentine	$2 \cdot 90 \times 10^5$
Water	$22 \cdot 6 \times 10^5$

SI Prefixes and Multiplication Factors

Prefix	Symbol	Factor	
giga	G	1 000 000 000	$= 10^9$
mega	M	1 000 000	$= 10^6$
kilo	k	1000	$= 10^3$
milli	m	0·001	$= 10^{-3}$
micro	μ	0·000 001	$= 10^{-6}$
nano	n	0·000 000 001	$= 10^{-9}$

Marks | K&U | PS

1. A farm road joins a main road at a bend. The farmer has placed a mirror as shown so that he can see when cars are approaching.

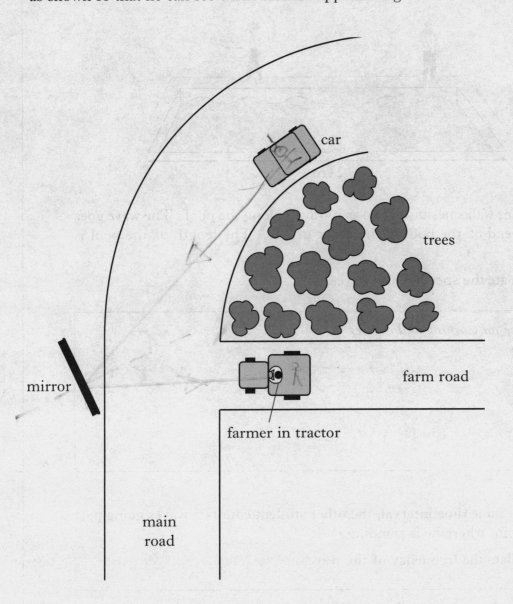

car

trees

mirror

farm road

farmer in tractor

main road

(a) On the diagram, draw rays to show how the farmer in the tractor can see the car by using the mirror.

You must label the angle of incidence and the angle of reflection on your completed diagram.

3

(b) State why the driver of the car can **also** see the tractor using the mirror.

....

.... 1

Page three **[Turn over**

Marks   K&U   PS

2. Two students watch the waves produced by a wave machine at a swimming pool.

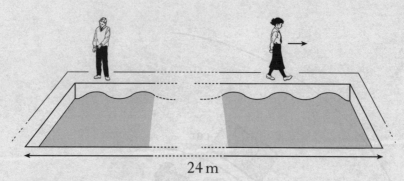

24 m

One student walks beside a wave as it travels along the pool. The wave goes from one end of the pool to the other in 20 s. The length of the pool is 24 m.

(*a*) Calculate the speed of the waves.

Space for working and answer

2

(*b*) In the same time interval, the other student counts 5 waves going past the point where he is standing.

Calculate the frequency of the waves.

Space for working and answer

2

DO NOT WRITE IN THIS MARGIN

Marks	K&U	PS

2. (continued)

(*c*) The students note that there are 5 complete waves in the pool at any time.

Calculate the wavelength of the waves.

Space for working and answer

2

(*d*) Explain why "distance divided by time" and "frequency times wavelength" are equivalent for a wave.

Space for working and answer

2

[Turn over

Marks | K&U | PS

3. A home entertainment centre consists of four appliances. The table gives the power rating of each appliance.

Appliance	Power rating (W)
television	110
video recorder	22
satellite receiver	20
DVD player	18

To operate properly, each appliance must be connected to mains voltage. The appliances are connected to the mains using a multiway adaptor.

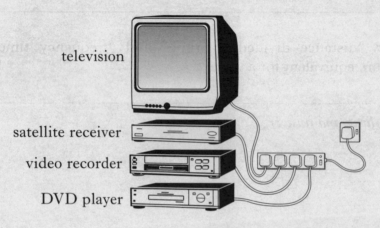

television

satellite receiver

video recorder

DVD player

(a) (i) State the value of the operating voltage of the appliances.

.... 1

(ii) The connections in the multiway adaptor are arranged to ensure that each appliance is connected to mains voltage.

State how the connections in the multiway adaptor are arranged to achieve this.

.... 1

(b) Calculate the current from the mains when all four appliances are operating at the power ratings shown in the table.

(You must use an appropriate number of significant figures in your answer to this question.)

Space for working and answer

3

Marks | K&U | PS

3. (continued)

(c) Calculate the resistance of the television when it is operating at the power rating stated in the table.

> *Space for working and answer*

2

(d) The plug on the flex of the multiway adaptor contains a fuse.

What is the purpose of this fuse?

....

....

.... 1

[Turn over

Marks | K&U | PS

4. A show uses five spotlights of equal brightness, pointing at the same place on the stage.

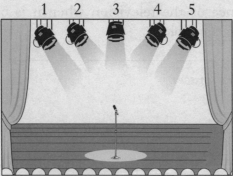

The spotlights can be turned on and off individually. The colour of light from each spotlight is shown in the table.

Spotlight	Colour
1	green
2	blue
3	red
4	blue
5	green

(a) State **three** spotlights that could be on to produce white light on the stage.

....

.... 1

(b) One scene requires yellow light.

State **two** spotlights that could be on to produce yellow light on the stage.

....

.... 1

(c) Another scene requires **pale** green light. This needs **four** of the spotlights to be on.

State **one** spotlight that could be **off** so that the other four produce pale green light.

.... 1

Marks | K&U | PS

5. A textbook has three diagrams showing how an eye lens changes when looking at objects that are different distances away. The diagrams below are copies of these three diagrams, with parts omitted.

Diagrams 1 and 3 are not complete.

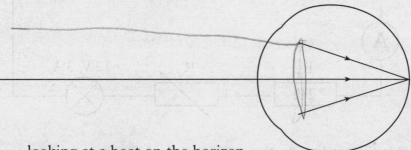

Diagram 1   looking at a boat on the horizon

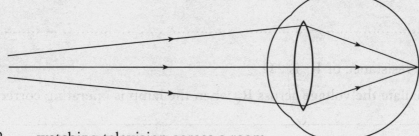

Diagram 2   watching television across a room

Diagram 3   reading small print in a book

(a) On diagrams 1 **and** 3:

   (i) draw two rays to show light coming from each object to the eye;

   (ii) draw a lens to show how the shape of the eye lens is different from the shape of the lens in diagram 2.

4

(b) The focal length of an eye lens system (the cornea and the eye lens together) is 2·5 cm.

Calculate the power of this eye lens system.

Space for working and answer

2

Marks | K&U | PS

6. A student designs the circuit shown to operate a 12 V, 3 A lamp from a 36 V supply.

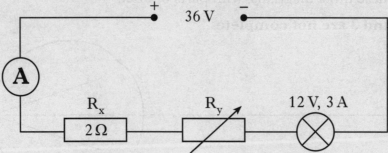

(a) What is the reading on the ammeter when the lamp is operating at its correct power rating?

.... **1**

(b) The resistance of R_x is $2\,\Omega$.

Calculate the voltage across R_x when the lamp is operating correctly.

Space for working and answer

2

(c) Calculate the resistance of R_y when the lamp is operating correctly.

Space for working and answer

3

Marks K&U PS

6. (continued)

(*d*) The student connects a second, identical lamp as shown in the diagram below.

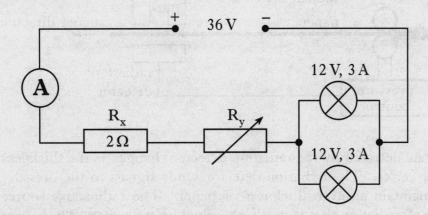

Explain why the resistance of R_y has to be adjusted for both lamps to operate correctly.

....

....

.... 2

[Turn over

Page eleven

Marks | K&U | PS

7. A paper mill uses a radioactive source in a system to monitor the thickness of paper.

The count rate detected by the radiation detector changes as the thickness of the paper varies. The radiation detector sends signals to the pressure control to maintain an even thickness of paper. The radioactive source emits a type of radiation that is partly absorbed by the paper. The source also has a half-life that allows the mill to run continuously, for several days.

(a) What is meant by the term "half-life"?

....

.... 1

(b) The following radioactive sources are available.

Source	Half-life	Radiation emitted
P	500 years	alpha
Q	20 hours	beta
R	450 years	beta
S	300 years	gamma

(i) Explain why source P cannot be used in this system.

....

....

.... 1

(ii) Which source should be used? Explain your answer.

....

....

.... 2

Marks | K&U | PS

7. **(continued)**

(c) Why does the radioactive source in the paper mill have a metal shield?

....

.... 1

(d) Another radioactive source emits gamma radiation. The graph shows how the activity of this source decreases with time.

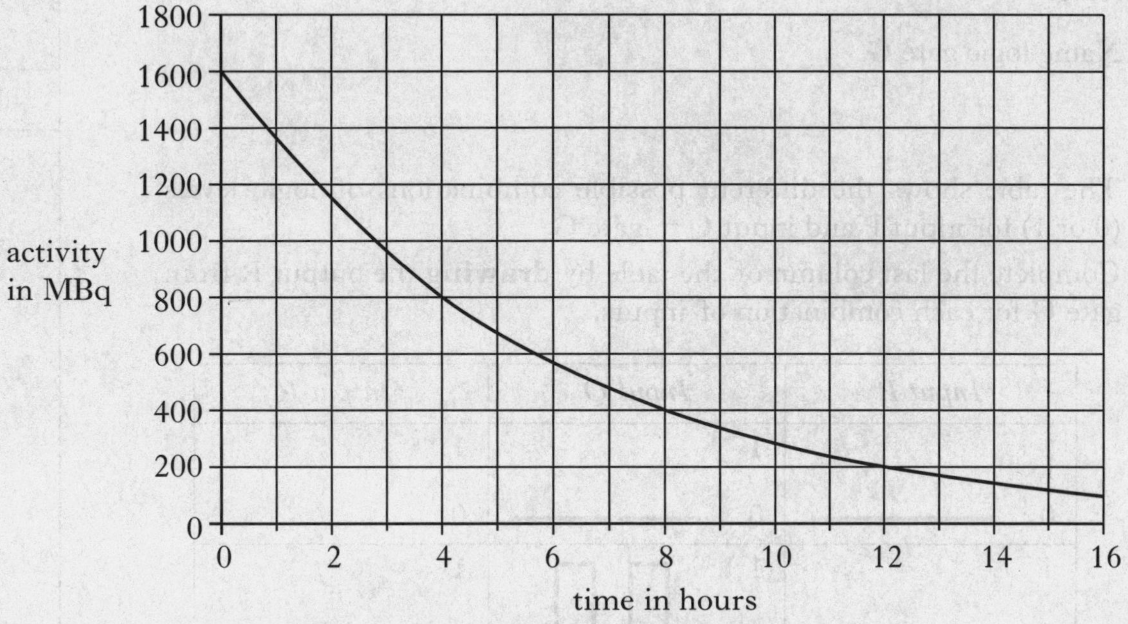

activity in MBq (y-axis, 0 to 1800)

time in hours (x-axis, 0 to 16)

Calculate the half-life of this radioactive source.

Space for working and answer

1

[Turn over

Marks | K&U | PS

8. A bus is fitted with a buzzer that sounds only when the bus is reversing. Part of the circuit that operates the buzzer is shown.

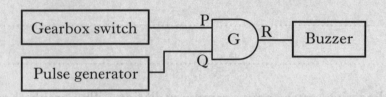

The output from the gearbox switch is high (logic 1) when the bus is reversing.

(*a*) Name logic gate G.

.... **1**

(*b*) The table shows the different possible combinations of logic levels (0 or 1) for input P and input Q to gate G.

Complete the last column of the table by **drawing** the output R from gate G for each combination of inputs.

Input P	Input Q	Output R
1	1	1
0 —————	0 —————	0
1	1 ⊓⊔⊓	1
0 —————	0 ⊔⊔⊔	0
1 —————	1	1
0	0 —————	0
1 —————	1 ⊓⊔⊓	1
0	0 ⊔⊔⊔	0

2

(*c*) The pulse generator part of the circuit is shown below.

The power supply to the NOT gate has been omitted for clarity.

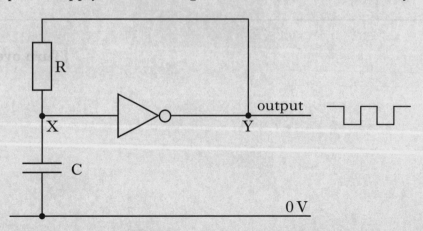

Marks

8. *(c)* **(continued)**

(i) Capacitor C is initially discharged.

Explain the operation of the pulse generator circuit, by referring to points X and Y in the circuit.

....

....

....

....

.... **2**

(ii) The pulse generator produces an output with a high frequency.

State **one** change that could be made to the circuit to give an output of lower frequency.

....

.... **1**

[Turn over

Marks | K&U | PS

9. An electronic circuit is shown below. Component R is a thermistor.

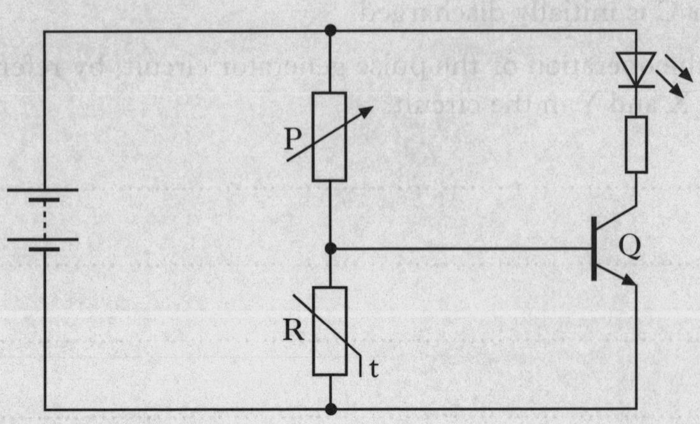

(a) Name component P.

.... 1

(b) (i) Name component Q.

.... 1

(ii) **In this circuit**, what is the function of component Q?

.... 1

(c) Explain how the circuit operates.

....

....

....

....

....

.... 2

Marks | K&U | PS

10. A cyclist starts a journey in first gear and uses two other gears during the journey. After a short time the cyclist is forced to brake sharply and comes to a halt. A speed-time graph of the journey is shown.

At point P the cyclist changes from first gear to second gear.
At point Q the cyclist changes from second gear to third gear.

(a) (i) Before braking, which gear is the cyclist using when the acceleration is greatest?

.... **1**

   (ii) Which gear does the cyclist use for the shortest time?

.... **1**

(b) Calculate how far the cyclist travels in second gear.

Space for working and answer

3

(c) Calculate the deceleration.

Space for working and answer

2

Marks

K&U PS

11. A model motor boat of mass 4 kg is initially at rest on a pond. The boat's motor, which provides a constant force of 5 N, is switched on. As the boat accelerates, the force of friction acting on it increases. A graph of the force of friction acting on the boat against time is shown.

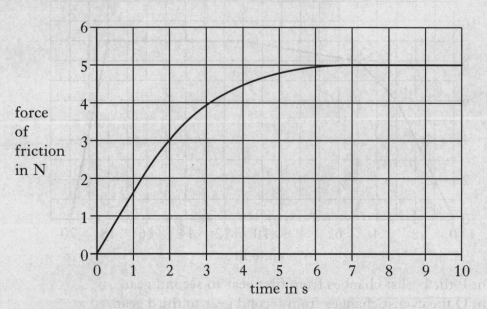

(a) (i) State the force of friction acting on the boat 2 s after the motor is switched on.

.... 1

(ii) Calculate the acceleration of the boat at this time.

> *Space for working and answer*

3

(b) Describe and explain the movement of the boat after 7 s.

....

....

.... 2

DO NOT WRITE IN THIS MARGIN

12. A battery charger with an input voltage of 230 V is used to recharge a car *Marks* battery. The charger contains a transformer that has an output voltage of 13·8 V.

(a) What type of transformer does the battery charger contain?

....

1

(b) There are 4000 turns in the primary coil of the transformer.

Assuming the transformer is 100% efficient, calculate the number of turns in the secondary coil.

Space for working and answer

2

(c) (i) When charging the battery, the current in the secondary coil is 4·7 A.

(A) Calculate the power output of the transformer.

Space for working and answer

2

(B) In practice, the transformer is only 94% efficient.
Calculate the current in the primary coil.

Space for working and answer

3

(ii) State and explain **one** reason why a transformer is not 100% efficient.

....

....

....

2

Marks | K&U | PS

13. Water from a stream is used to drive a water wheel. The stream provides 6000 kg of water per minute to the wheel. The water falls a vertical height of 5 m.

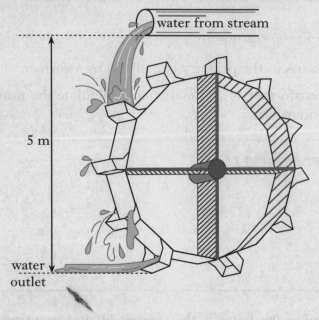

water from stream

5 m

water
outlet

(a) Show that the maximum power available to the wheel from the water is 5000 W.

> *Space for working and answer*

3

(b) The water wheel turns an electrical generator. The generator produces an output of 2990 W.

(i) Calculate the efficiency of the water wheel and generator system.

> *Space for working and answer*

2

Marks | K&U | PS

13. **(b)** **(continued)**

(ii) Give **two** reasons why the efficiency of this system is not 100%.

....

....

....

....

2

(iii) The generator is connected to a heater in a shed. The heater heats the air in the shed. The mass of air in the shed is 161 kg. The specific heat capacity of air is 1000 J/kg °C.

Calculate the minimum time to increase the temperature of the air in the shed by 13 °C.

Space for working and answer

3

(iv) Give **one** reason why the actual time taken to increase the temperature of the air in the shed is greater than the value calculated in (iii).

....

....

1

[Turn over

Marks | K&U | PS

14. Gamma rays, ultraviolet and infrared are three members of a family of waves. Every member of this family travels at the speed of light.

(a) What name is given to this family of waves?

.... **1**

(b) Some uses of waves in this family are shown below.

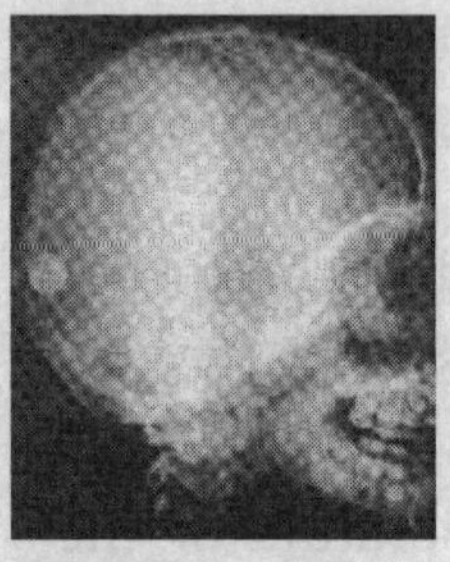

Photographing
bones inside a
body

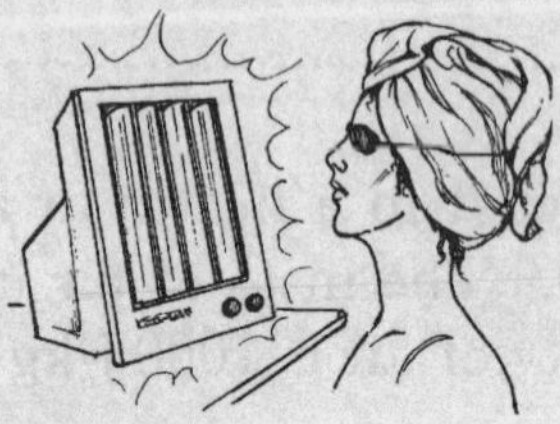

Tanning with a
sun-ray lamp

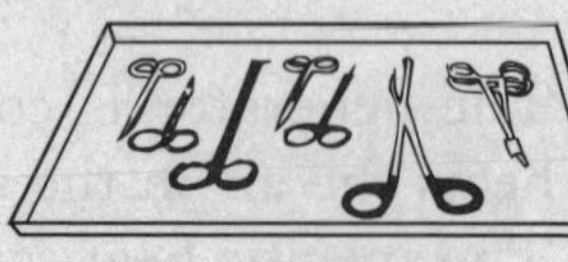

Sterilising medical
instruments

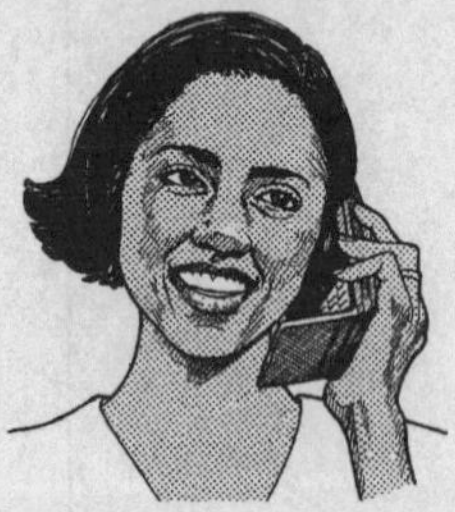

Communicating
with mobile
phones

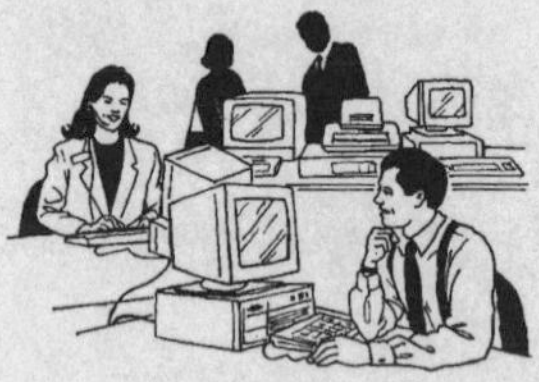

Linking networked
computers through
optical fibres

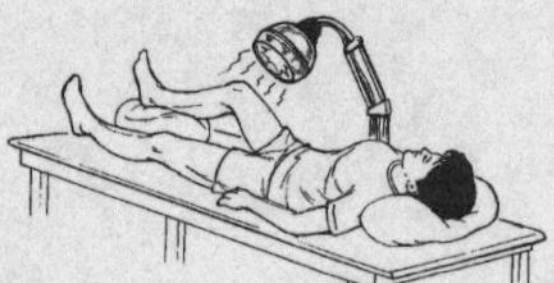

Treating injuries
using a heat-lamp

(i) From the examples above, give a use for:

gamma rays..

ultraviolet ....

infrared... **3**

(ii) Which of the three waves in (i) has:

the longest wavelength ....

the highest frequency? **2**

Marks | K&U | PS

15. A darts player throws a dart horizontally at the centre of the inner bull. The dart leaves the player's hand at a distance of 2·16 m from the dartboard and with a horizontal speed of 12·0 m/s.

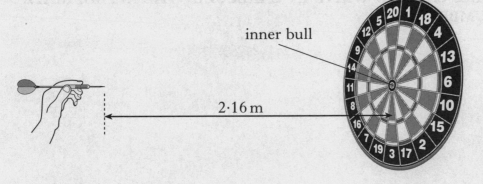

inner bull

2·16 m

(a) Calculate the time taken for the dart to travel from the hand to the board.

> *Space for working and answer*

2

(b) Explain why the dart follows a curved path in its flight to the board.

....

....

....

2

(c) The average vertical speed of the dart during its flight to the board is 0·9 m/s.

How far below the centre of the inner bull does the dart hit the board?

> *Space for working and answer*

2

[END OF QUESTION PAPER]

K&U	PS

YOU MAY USE THE SPACE ON THIS PAGE TO REWRITE ANY ANSWER YOU HAVE DECIDED TO CHANGE IN THE MAIN PART OF THE ANSWER BOOKLET. TAKE CARE TO WRITE IN CAREFULLY THE APPROPRIATE QUESTION NUMBER.

C

FOR OFFICIAL USE

K & U	PS

Total Marks

3220/402

NATIONAL
QUALIFICATIONS
2004

FRIDAY, 28 MAY
10.50 AM – 12.35 PM

PHYSICS
STANDARD GRADE
Credit Level

Fill in these boxes and read what is printed below.

Full name of centre

Town

Forename(s)

Surname

Date of birth
Day Month Year   Scottish candidate number   Number of seat

1 All questions should be answered.

2 The questions may be answered in any order but all answers must be written clearly and legibly in this book.

3 Write your answer where indicated by the question or in the space provided after the question.

4 If you change your mind about your answer you may score it out and rewrite it in the space provided at the end of the answer book.

5 Before leaving the examination room you must give this book to the invigilator. If you do not, you may lose all the marks for this paper.

6 Any necessary data will be found in the **data sheet** on page two.

7 Care should be taken to give an appropriate number of significant figures in the final answers to questions.

SCOTTISH
QUALIFICATIONS
AUTHORITY

DATA SHEET

Speed of light in materials

Material	Speed in m/s
Air	$3 \cdot 0 \times 10^8$
Carbon dioxide	$3 \cdot 0 \times 10^8$
Diamond	$1 \cdot 2 \times 10^8$
Glass	$2 \cdot 0 \times 10^8$
Glycerol	$2 \cdot 1 \times 10^8$
Water	$2 \cdot 3 \times 10^8$

Speed of sound in materials

Material	Speed in m/s
Aluminium	5200
Air	340
Bone	4100
Carbon dioxide	270
Glycerol	1900
Muscle	1600
Steel	5200
Tissue	1500
Water	1500

Gravitational field strengths

	Gravitational field strength on the surface in N/kg
Earth	10
Jupiter	26
Mars	4
Mercury	4
Moon	$1 \cdot 6$
Neptune	12
Saturn	11
Sun	270
Venus	9

Specific heat capacity of materials

Material	Specific heat capacity in J/kg °C
Alcohol	2350
Aluminium	902
Copper	386
Diamond	530
Glass	500
Glycerol	2400
Ice	2100
Lead	128
Water	4180

Specific latent heat of fusion of materials

Material	Specific latent heat of fusion in J/kg
Alcohol	$0 \cdot 99 \times 10^5$
Aluminium	$3 \cdot 95 \times 10^5$
Carbon dioxide	$1 \cdot 80 \times 10^5$
Copper	$2 \cdot 05 \times 10^5$
Glycerol	$1 \cdot 81 \times 10^5$
Lead	$0 \cdot 25 \times 10^5$
Water	$3 \cdot 34 \times 10^5$

Melting and boiling points of materials

Material	Melting point in °C	Boiling point in °C
Alcohol	−98	65
Aluminium	660	2470
Copper	1077	2567
Glycerol	18	290
Lead	328	1737
Turpentine	−10	156

Specific latent heat of vaporisation of materials

Material	Specific latent heat of vaporisation in J/kg
Alcohol	$11 \cdot 2 \times 10^5$
Carbon dioxide	$3 \cdot 77 \times 10^5$
Glycerol	$8 \cdot 30 \times 10^5$
Turpentine	$2 \cdot 90 \times 10^5$
Water	$22 \cdot 6 \times 10^5$

SI Prefixes and Multiplication Factors

Prefix	Symbol	Factor	
giga	G	1 000 000 000	$= 10^9$
mega	M	1 000 000	$= 10^6$
kilo	k	1000	$= 10^3$
milli	m	0·001	$= 10^{-3}$
micro	μ	0·000 001	$= 10^{-6}$
nano	n	0·000 000 001	$= 10^{-9}$

Marks

1. A mobile phone can send signals on 3 different frequencies, 900 MHz, 1800 MHz and 1900 MHz.

    (a) (i) Which signal has the longest wavelength?

    .... **1**

    (ii) Calculate the wavelength of the 1800 MHz signal.

    ┌───┐
    │ *Space for working and answer*   │
    │   │
    │   │
    │   │
    │   │
    │   │
    └───┘ **3**

    (b) At a base station, microwave signals from the mobile phone are converted into light signals for transmission along an optical fibre.

    (i) State two advantages of sending light signals along an optical fibre compared to sending electrical signals along a wire.

    ....

    .... **2**

    (ii) The time taken for light to travel along a glass optical fibre is 1·2 ms.

    (A) State the speed at which signals travel along the optical fibre.

    .... **1**

    (B) Calculate the length of the optical fibre.

    ┌───┐
    │ *Space for working and answer*   │
    │   │
    │   │
    │   │
    │   │
    │   │
    └───┘ **2**

Marks | K&U | PS

2. A colour television receiver displays 25 images on the screen every second.

(a) Calculate the number of images displayed on the screen in one minute.

> *Space for working and answer*

1

(b) The television receiver contains decoders.

State the function of a decoder.

....

.... 1

(c) In the colour television tube, three electron guns each send a beam of electrons to the screen.

(i) Why are **three** electron guns needed in a **colour** television tube?

....

.... 1

(ii) The diagram below shows the screen and the shadow mask in a colour television tube.

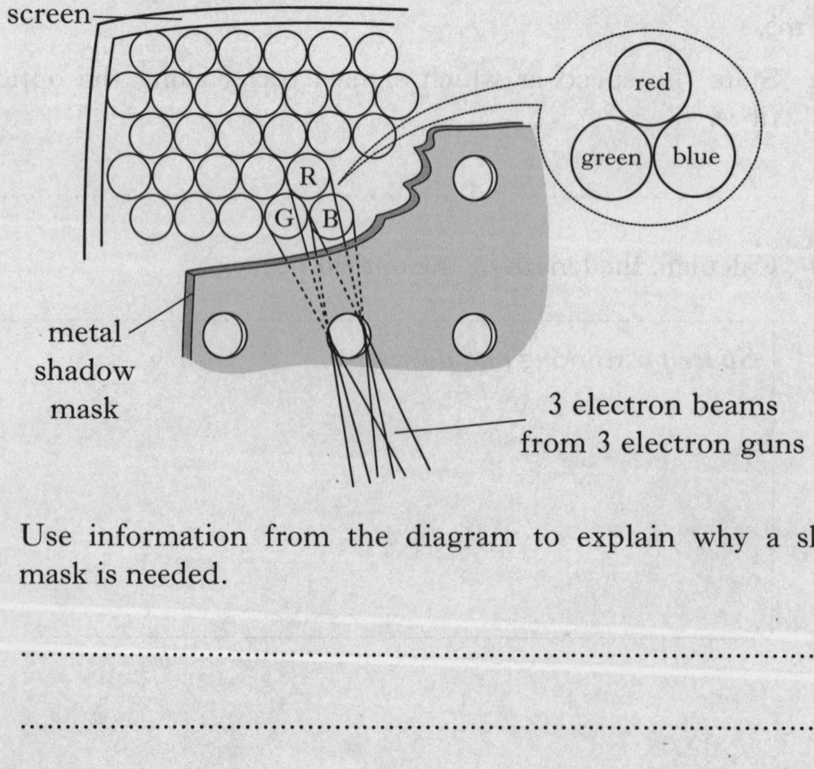

Use information from the diagram to explain why a shadow mask is needed.

....

....

.... 2

Marks   K&U   PS

3. A portable radio contains a rechargeable battery and a generator. The battery is charged by turning the handle of the generator.

(a) State the purpose of the battery.

....   **1**

(b) The battery is fully discharged. The handle of the generator is turned 500 times by a constant force of 9·0 N. For each turn of the handle, the force moves through a distance of 400 mm.

   (i) Show that the work done in charging the battery is 1800 J.

Space for working and answer

  2

   (ii) Only 90% of the work done in charging the battery is available as output energy from the battery.

     (A) Calculate the output energy available.

Space for working and answer

  2

     (B) When operating, the radio takes a current of 250 mA. The voltage of the battery is 3 V.

     Calculate the maximum time for which the radio operates.

Space for working and answer

  2

Marks K&U PS

4. The circuit diagram of the wiring of a car's sidelights and headlights is shown.

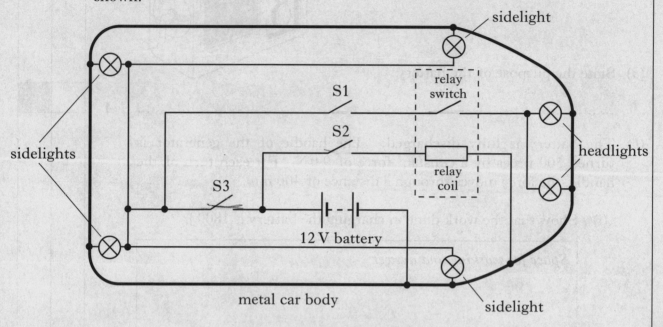

S1 is the headlight switch. S2 is the ignition switch.

When there is a current in the relay coil, the relay switch closes.

(*a*) Which lights are on when switch S3 **only** is closed?

.... 1

(*b*) At night the car has the sidelights on and the headlights on. The driver switches off the ignition. This opens the ignition switch.

Explain why **only** the headlights go out.

....

....

.... 2

Marks | K&U | PS

4. **(continued)**

(c) **Each** sidelight is rated at 12 V, 6 W, and **each** headlight is rated at 12 V, 55 W.

   (i) Calculate the current in the battery when **only** the sidelights are on.

Space for working and answer

          3

   (ii) The driver leaves the car for 10 minutes with **only** the sidelights on.

Calculate the charge that flows through the battery in this time.

Space for working and answer

          2

   (iii) Each headlight gives out more light energy than each sidelight when on for the same time.

Explain why this happens.

....

....

.... 2

[Turn over

Marks | K&U | PS

5. An entry system for a block of flats lets residents speak to callers before unlocking the outside door.

(a) A microphone at the outside door is connected through an amplifier to a loudspeaker in a flat.

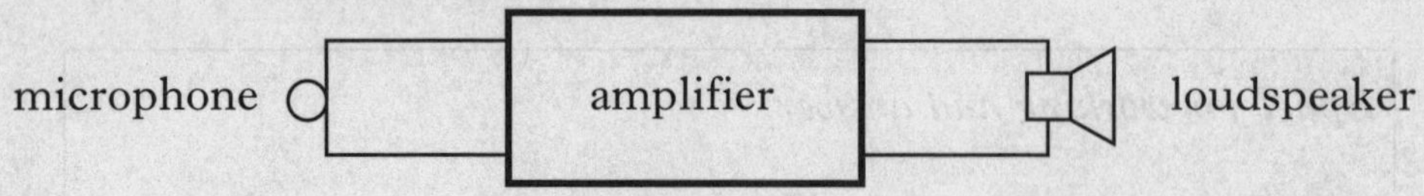

microphone ○ ⊐▭⊏ amplifier ⊐▭⊏ ◁ loudspeaker

The input power to the amplifier from the microphone is 5 mW and the output power from the amplifier is 2 W.

(i) Calculate the power gain of the amplifier.

Space for working and answer

2

(ii) The voltage across the loudspeaker is 4 V.

Calculate the resistance (impedance) of the loudspeaker.

Space for working and answer

2

Marks | K&U | PS

5. (continued)

(b) The entry system allows a resident to unlock the outside door from the flat. The diagram below shows this part of this system.

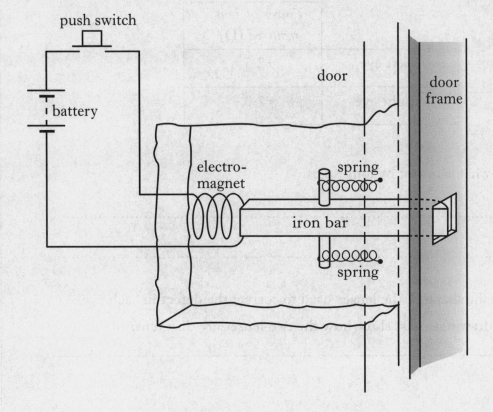

Explain how this part of the system operates to unlock the door.

....

....

....

.... 2

[Turn over

Marks | K&U | PS

6. A person visits an optician for an eye test and is found to be long sighted in both eyes. The optician issues the following prescription for lenses.

	Power of lens required (D)
Left eye	+2·5
Right eye	+1·0

(a) State what is meant by long sight.

....

.... **1**

(b) Draw the shape of the lenses used to correct the defect in each eye.

Your drawings must show how the two lenses are different.

Shape of lens for left eye	
Shape of lens for right eye	

3

(c) Calculate the focal length of the lens prescribed for the left eye.

Space for working and answer

2

Marks | K&U | PS

7. A smoke detector contains two metal electrodes, a battery and an alarm circuit. Alpha radiation from a radioactive source ionises air between the two electrodes.

A voltage is applied across the electrodes. Although there is a gap between the two electrodes, there is a current between the electrodes. When there are smoke particles between the electrodes, this current is reduced. This sets off the alarm.

(a) (i) What is meant by ionisation?

....

.... **1**

(ii) Explain how the current is produced in the gap between the electrodes.

....

.... **1**

(b) Apart from safety reasons, why is a source that emits alpha radiation more suitable in a smoke detector than a source that emits gamma radiation?

....

.... **1**

(c) State the unit of activity of a radioactive source.

.... **1**

Marks | K&U | PS

8. At a bottling plant, shampoo bottles on a conveyor pass a liquid level
    detector. Bottles filled to an acceptable level continue along the conveyor
    for packing. Bottles that are overfilled or underfilled are rejected.

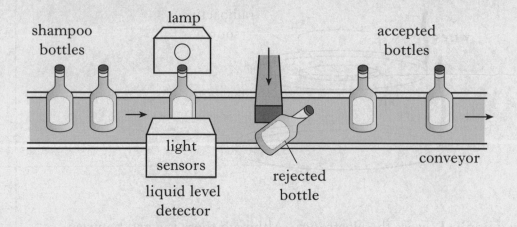

The liquid level detector consists of a lamp and two identical light sensors.
The sensors are placed as shown in the diagram below. Light from the
lamp can reach a sensor only when there is no shampoo between the lamp
and the sensor.

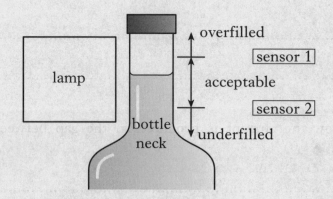

Part of the logic circuit of the liquid level detector is shown below.

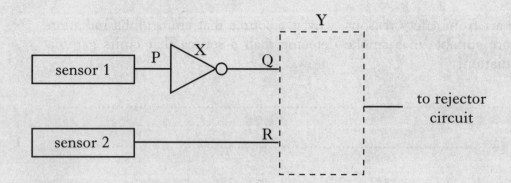

DO NOT WRITE IN THIS MARGIN

Marks | K&U | PS

8. (continued)

The logic level outputs of a light sensor are as shown.

Light level at sensor	*Logic level output*
dark	0
light	1

(*a*) Name gate X.

.... **1**

(*b*) Complete the table to show the logic levels at P, Q and R when bottles filled to different levels are at the detector.

Liquid level	**P**	**Q**	**R**
Overfilled			
Acceptable			
Underfilled			

3

(*c*) The rejector circuit requires a logic level 1 to operate.

What type of gate at Y gives a logic 1 output only when a bottle is not filled to an acceptable level?

.... **1**

[Turn over

Marks | K&U | PS

9. Land speed records are calculated by timing a vehicle as it travels a measured distance of 2·0 km.

(a) Explain whether the average speed or the instantaneous speed of the vehicle can be calculated from these measurements.

....

....

.... **2**

(b) A vehicle travels the measured distance at a constant speed of 220 m/s. Calculate the time taken.

Space for working and answer

2

(c) At the end of the measured distance, the driver switches off the engine and opens a parachute to brake.

The speed-time graph shows the motion of the vehicle from this time.

The mass of the vehicle is 3000 kg.

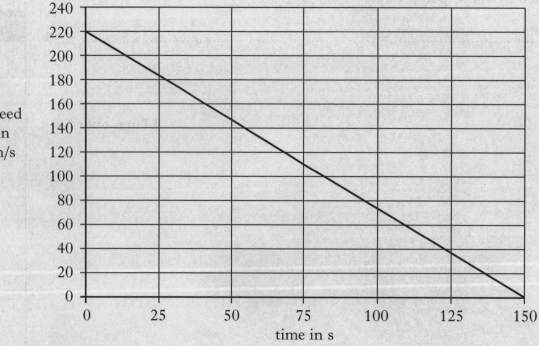

Marks | K&U | PS

9. **(c)** **(continued)**

(i) Explain how the parachute helps to reduce the speed of the vehicle.

....

....   1

(ii) Calculate the distance travelled by the vehicle from the time the parachute opens until the vehicle stops.

Space for working and answer

2

(iii) Calculate the acceleration of the vehicle while it is slowing down.

Space for working and answer

2

(iv) Calculate the unbalanced force on the vehicle while it is slowing down.

Space for working and answer

2

[Turn over

Marks | K&U | PS

9. (c) (continued)

(v) Calculate the kinetic energy of the vehicle at the instant the parachute opens.

Space for working and answer

2

10. A metal guitar string, fixed to a wooden base, is connected to an oscilloscope. A magnet is placed so that the string is between the poles of the magnet, as shown.

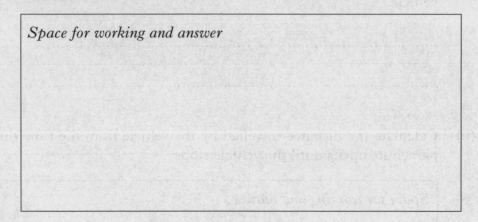

When the string is plucked, a sound is produced and a voltage is induced in the string. The induced voltage is displayed on the screen of the oscilloscope.

(a) (i) Why is a voltage induced when the string is plucked?

....

.... 1

(ii) State one change that can be made so that a larger voltage is induced.

.... 1

Marks | K&U | PS

10. **(continued)**

(b) The oscilloscope gain setting and trace are shown.

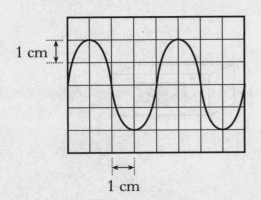

GAIN

Calculate the peak voltage.

Space for working and answer

2

(c) A different metal string is used to produce a louder sound of higher frequency. No other changes are made to the equipment.

Draw a possible new trace on the blank screen below.

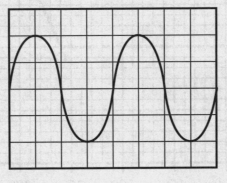

trace produced
by original
string

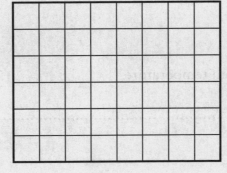

trace produced
by second
string

2

Marks | K&U | PS

11. A mass of 500 g of a substance is heated with a 30 W heater. A temperature probe is inserted into the substance.

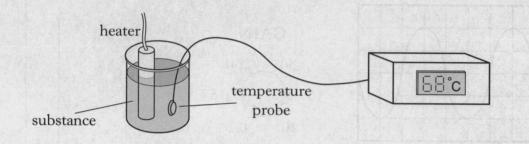

The substance is initially solid and at room temperature. The graph below shows the variation of the temperature of the substance from the time the heater is switched on.

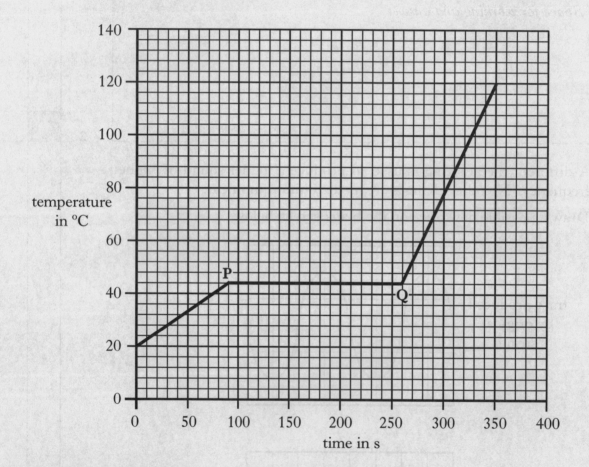

(a) State the value of room temperature.

.... **1**

DO NOT WRITE IN THIS MARGIN

Marks K&U PS

11. (continued)

(*b*) (i) Why does the temperature of the substance remain constant between P and Q?

.... 1

(ii) Calculate the energy transferred by the heater during the time interval PQ.

Space for working and answer

3

(iii) Calculate the specific latent heat of fusion of the substance.

Space for working and answer

2

[Turn over

Marks | K&U | PS

12. A bicycle lamp contains four LEDs W, X, Y and Z and a 3 V battery. The lamp uses a pulse generator to make two of the LEDs flash. A simplified circuit diagram of the bicycle lamp is shown.

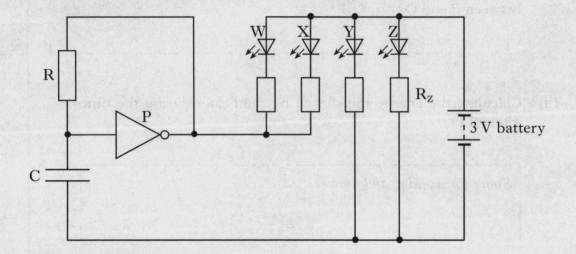

(a) (i) Which LEDs flash when the lamp is operating?

.... **1**

(ii) State two changes that could be made to the circuit to increase the frequency at which the LEDs flash.

....

.... **2**

(b) When LED Z is lit, the current in it is 15 mA and the voltage across it is 1·8 V.

Calculate the resistance of R_Z.

Space for working and answer

3

Page twenty

Marks | K&U | PS

13. The table below has information about three telescopes used to detect radiation from space.

objective lens	Refracting telescope in Edinburgh, with 150 mm diameter objective lens.
detector / curved reflector	Radio telescope at Jodrell Bank, with a curved reflector of diameter 76 m.
detector / curved reflector	Radio telescope at Arecibo, Puerto Rico, with a curved reflector of diameter 300 m.

(a) What type of radiation is detected by a refracting telescope?

.... 1

(b) Why are different types of telescope used to detect radiation from space?

....

.... 1

(c) In a radio telescope, where is the detector placed in relation to the curved reflector?

....

.... 1

(d) Explain which of the three telescopes shown above is best for detecting very weak radio signals from deep space.

....

....

....

.... 2

Marks | K&U | PS

14. A space vehicle consists of a rocket engine, fuel and a probe. When sitting on the launch pad, the total mass of the space vehicle is 150 000 kg.

(a) Calculate the weight of the space vehicle on the launch pad.

> *Space for working and answer*

2

(b) The space vehicle is launched. Shortly after lift-off, it is at a height of 650 km above the surface of the Earth. At this time, 80 000 kg of fuel have been used.

Give **two** reasons why the weight of the space vehicle is now less than it was on the launch pad.

Reason one...

....

Reason two ....

....

2

(c) The space vehicle travels into a region of space where the gravitational field strength is zero. The engine is now switched off.

Describe and explain the motion of the vehicle.

....

....

....

2

DO NOT WRITE IN THIS MARGIN

Marks K&U PS

15. Some members of the electromagnetic spectrum are named below.

TV and Radio	Infrared	Visible light		X-rays	Gamma rays

(*a*) Write the names of the missing radiations in the correct spaces in the diagram above. **2**

(*b*) State **one** radiation that has a lower frequency than visible light.

.... **1**

(*c*) State **one** detector of X-rays.

.... **1**

(*d*) State **one** medical use of infrared radiation.

.... **1**

[*END OF QUESTION PAPER*]

YOU MAY USE THE SPACE ON THIS PAGE TO REWRITE ANY ANSWER YOU HAVE DECIDED TO CHANGE IN THE MAIN PART OF THE ANSWER BOOKLET. TAKE CARE TO WRITE IN CAREFULLY THE APPROPRIATE QUESTION NUMBER.

[BLANK PAGE]

[BLANK PAGE]